CW00541687

Paris or Die

Jayne Tuttle

Hardie Grant

BOOKS

First published in 2019
This edition published in 2022 by Hardie Grant Books,
an imprint of Hardie Grant Publishing

Hardie Grant Books (Melbourne)
Wurundjeri Country
Building 1, 658 Church Street
Richmond, Victoria 3121

Hardie Grant Books (London)
5th & 6th Floors
52–54 Southwark Street
London SE1 1UN

hardiegrantbooks.com

 A catalogue record for this
book is available from the
National Library of Australia

Paris or Die
ISBN 978 1 74379 830 0

10 9 8 7 6 5 4 3 2 1

Cover design by Jo Thomson
Cover image: Sang Ho Kim/Eye Em via Getty Images
Typeset in Minion 11/15pt by Cannon Typesetting
Printed in Australia by Griffin Press, an Accredited ISO AS/NZS 14001
Environmental Management System printer.

The paper this book is printed on is certified against the
Forest Stewardship Council® Standards. Griffin Press holds
chain of custody certification SGSHK-COC-005088. FSC®
promotes environmentally responsible, socially beneficial
and economically viable management of the world's forests.

Hardie Grant acknowledges the Traditional Owners of the country on which we work,
the Wurundjeri people of the Kulin nation and the Gadigal people of the Eora nation,
and recognises their continuing connection to the land, waters and culture. We pay our
respects to their Elders past and present.

PRAISE FOR *PARIS OR DIE*

'By turns madcap and heart-breaking, *Paris or Die* is a witty and wise reflection on the power of cities to help us become ourselves. I devoured it and I can't wait to read more from my new favorite writer.' Lauren Elkin, author of *Flâneuse: Women Walk the City, No 91/92: A Diary of a Year on the Bus*, translator of Simone de Beauvoir's *The Inseparables*

'A vivid memoir of damage, grace and healing which manages to be funny, irreverent and moving all at once.' Luke Davies, author of *Candy*, *Totem*, script writer of *Lion*

'Jayne Tuttle's writing is a delicious delight.' Christos Tsiolkas, author of *The Slap*, *Damascus*, *Seven and a Half*

'An electric rollercoaster ride through the streets of Paris, this is also a moving memoir of love, exploration and loss – at times utterly joyful, at times gut-wrenching and always fierce and beautifully written.' Jemma Birrell, *Tablo Tales*, *The Secret Life of Writers*

'I was entranced from start to finish. A tantalising tour through the life of a young, spontaneous, in love, in lust, foreigner whose inimitable joie de vivre opens her to a Paris that yields its local charms, its particular customs and its unexpected dangers ...' Martine Murray, author of *The Last Summer of Ada Bloom*, *How to Make a Bird*

'A riveting, moving, funny and at times shocking memoir about a young Australian woman whose dream journey to the city of light turns into a nightmare. I loved it.' Jennifer Higgie, author of *The Mirror and the Palette*, editor for *Frieze*

'Moving, raw and more than a little bit sexy, I practically inhaled this book about a woman determined to grab on to art, love and life with everything she's got in the world's most romantic city.' *Rachel Power, author of* The Divided Heart: Art and Motherhood

'Joyous, sexy and compelling ... a wonderful read.' Paddy O'Reilly, author of *Peripheral Vision*, *The Wonders*, *Other Houses*

For Niela, Lyn and Frankie

It was January. Paris was dark. Short sharp days bookended with long black night. Black in the apartment as my alarm went off, black in the stairwell as I fumbled for the light switch, indigo down the rue de la Chine, past the glow of the already buzzing boulangerie. Mahogany beneath my eyelids as I rattled through the underworld. Grey past the Panthéon to French class and all its subjunctives and conditionals and whatevers-it-took to keep my visa. Then black again: five pm in the Adrienless apartment, his absence thick in the damp winter air. I sat in the shadows thinking, Now what?

'Come at six o'clock,' said Sophie in her delicate French. 'I missed you,' she continued into the phone, which surprised and flattered me. We hadn't known each other long, and she had only been gone a week or two. I had forgotten I existed, let alone to new friends like her. I suddenly couldn't wait to see her. And Lou, her mini Frida Kahlo.

Five-fifteen. Some shopping on the rue des Pyrénées. A few pieces of fruit and three stinky cheeses. Two pear-and-chocolate *gourmandises* for Sophie and Lou. Turn back: one for me. The Christmas lights were still twinkling in the bare trees. As I was crossing the street admiring them, a man nearly collected me on his scooter. '*Pardooon,*' his voice trailed behind him. It was a close call but I didn't bother protesting. He was well and truly gone. Anyway, it was my own fault for trusting the walk sign.

Five forty-five. My kitchen window was frozen shut but I managed to lift it and place the cheeses out on the ledge – too stinky for the fridge.

Five-fifty. On my way out the door I turned back, threw off my sneakers, and put on the boots with the heel. A slash of lipstick. The girl in the mirror said, There you are.

I went down to the courtyard to get my bike. Luc, the owner of the restaurant on the ground floor, was there emptying a bottle bin. He told me I must come in soon and taste his new wine. 'With pleasure,' I smiled, and pushed through the foyer and out into the dark, damp street.

It started to rain as I rode down the rue de la Chine. It's crying, I thought to myself, remembering how Adrien had found it cute that I confused words like *pleurer* (cry) and *pleuvoir* (rain). It began to cry hard as I hit the boulevard, and straps of hair plastered my face as I wove through the traffic's never-ending insanity. An ambulance blared up the wrong side of the street. I sped through the intersection so as not to block it. By the time I locked up my bike in the rue Pelleport the rain had stopped, leaving the street a pool of coloured reflections.

Six o'clock, on the dot. I punched in Sophie's door code and pushed open the heavy glass door to enter her striking Art Deco foyer, with its diamond mirrors and chequered floors. Her building was so *authentic*. The ornate lift stood empty on the ground floor behind its intricate ironwork gate, but I didn't take it because I had a rule: under three, use your knees. Besides, it was a small building and the staircase was easy to climb, winding around the open lift shaft, within which the cabin moved freely up and down, its cables and pulleys invisible in the darkness. The protective banister was low, built for petite, mid-century French people, not tall, late-century Australians.

I paid no attention whatsoever to the lift or the liftwell or the low banister. The carpeted stairs felt lush beneath my feet. I took them two at a time.

There was no answer at Sophie's door. I pushed the gold nipple again. The desire to see them seared in me. Where *were* they?

'We're just arriving,' Sophie apologised into the phone, mumbling something about Lou's hands being dirty.

The big glass door downstairs clicked and banged shut, followed by the chatter of female voices, a man saying *bonsoir*.

'*Maman*,' said Lou's tiny voice, 'is Jayne already at our place?'

The padding of damp feet up the stairs. I moved a few steps down from the second-floor landing so I could see them. 'Lou! Up here!'

She looked up from the bottom of the staircase, dark eyes beneath their sweet monobrow searching for me as I peered down from on high. I could see her so clearly, pale skin glowing in the dim stairwell light, but she couldn't see me. Sophie murmured something and they continued walking up.

I waved. 'Loo-uu!'

Again she looked up, searching but not seeing. Her face was as bright as the moon, eyes dancing with the fun of the game. She *had* to see me. I leant a bit further over the banister to make myself visible.

And then.

A curious feeling.

I can see Sophie and Lou walking up the stairs but I can't play anymore. My head is stuck to the right, my neck jammed beneath something cold and metal. A great weight. I don't understand. A cool draught whistles in my left ear. My hands are still on the banister, my feet on the stairs. But my head won't move.

The urge to laugh. This can't be real. Sophie's curls are bouncing on the collar of her tan coat as she continues walking up, Lou is saying something about a purple rabbit. They seem close enough to touch and yet very far away. I try to call out to them but no sound comes.

A realisation: I can't breathe.

And then.

A clink of metal, a flash of light, the roar of an approaching train.

Then black.

Naïve

I arrived in Paris eight years earlier with an overstuffed backpack and no place to stay. I can see myself from above, sitting on the backpack in a polished stone square near the Palais Royal, dwarfed by the façade of the Hôtel du Louvre, the columns of the Comédie Française, and the bustling terrace of the Café Nemours. I am a small blot in the picture, not long twenty-two, the part in my hair turning rapidly pink in the hot afternoon sun. The heat has thrown me: I always pictured Paris as a perpetual snowdome. Sweat drips down my forehead as I sit jetlagged and delirious, staring at a bizarre, bejewelled space octopus.

'*Mademoiselle?*'

The octopus, made of silver and coloured glass balls, spreads its limbs over the entrance to a métro station – Palais Royal – from which people spill in and out, going places they know. The sun lights the glass balls like boiled sweets – blueberry, lemon, grape. I fantasise about sucking one, staring so long my eyes begin to water.

'*Mademoiselle?*' says the voice again and I realise it's talking to me. 'Do not crying.'

I stop rubbing my eyes. The silhouette of a lady stands a few steps away. She is all polka dots.

'I wasn't. *Merci.* I'm …'

'You are lost?'

Yes. Utterly, completely. All the hostels I've tried are full. I have no idea how I got here or what I am doing in this scorching square in a duffel coat, wanting to suck an octopus leg. All I did was sit down in an airtight chamber in Melbourne twenty-seven hours ago, next to a German called Albert who gave me tissues as I wept, watching the silhouettes of my family in the airport lounge window wave slowly back and forth. Lost? Yes.

Though I suppose I've always been coming to Paris. Ever since the new French teacher in high school brought in croissants and films starring Vincent Perez. Since Chris took the place next to me in French class. Since he said *je t'aime* and took my virginity. I'd kept on with French at university because I didn't know what else to do, and by then I quite liked it. Even the verb tables. And especially transcription classes, trying to decipher the words in films, pressing rewind and pause until my finger got an arrow-shaped groove in it. That's how I discovered *Betty Blue*, and decided to be her, wielding big sighs and new sex things on Chris, who was titillated but unsure. Then he dumped me under his mum's willow tree. It wasn't the sex or the sighs; he wasn't sure he'd ever loved me. He wasn't sure what love meant. I wanted to die. Then, I figured, if I was going to end it, I might as well cut my hair off, dye it Betty Blue black, and go to Paris.

I abandoned my honours year and took two jobs, working nine am until two am, seven days a week. When my account read five thousand dollars I quit both jobs and bought a ticket. My friends at the day job gave me a passport wallet. My friends at the night job gave me the backpack. Kevin, a drunk guy from the night job, gave me a lucky penny. Dad gave me the laughing Buddha he'd had next to his alarm clock forever. Mum gave me her Special Dress. My brothers gave me a Swiss Army knife. My sister drilled a hole in the lucky penny, put it on a necklace made of string, and slipped it into the backpack with a note: *Come back soon, arsehole.*

'*Mademoiselle?* I can help you?'

The lady materialises. A middle-aged brunette in a prim grey skirt.

'*Merci*,' I say, squeezing the penny around my neck. '*Non*, I'm fine. I just can't find a room. Everything … *complet*.'

She furrows her delicate eyebrows. 'Do not worrying. I will 'elp you finding zomesing. I am 'aving a friend.'

She pulls a phone from her bag and walks across the square, sending pigeons fluttering. Her stockings have little bows up the back. From behind she looks like Madame Cherubim, my first-year French professor. Her name meant Little Angel but she was a Big Bitch. The back of this lady's neck is svelte, like a ballerina's. She wouldn't slam a door in my face. She wouldn't laugh at my accent as I read aloud from *Le Monde*.

She finishes her call and clips back to me, concern on her face. I notice she has one eye that looks out to the side, of its own volition.

'It is very difficult because it is May and, you know, it is *touristes*.' The eye clicks back into place. 'But my friend is 'aving an 'ôtel on the avenue Ledru-Rollin and she is 'aving one room. Not a good room. But a room. I write it down.'

I don't know why she doesn't include me as a tourist, and fantasise for a moment that she thinks I'm French. A hilarious thought, given my ridiculous winter coat, dirty boots, and disastrous hair with blond roots coming through. I don't know where the avenue Ladoo Roller is, but say *merci* to the lady, who hands me a torn piece of paper, says, '*Courage*,' and disappears into the octopus.

The little red street guide is deep in my satchel, amongst the cracker crumbs and boarding passes. A card with the words *Bon Voyage* written on the curved sail of a ship falls from the book as I pull it out, with Mum's neat cursive message inside: *Our dear petite fille, have a wonderful adventure!*

A pang of homesickness – swallowed. Twelfth arrondissement. Ledru-Rollin. The guidebook tells me the avenue is not far, but it's a little book, so distances might be deceiving. I decide to take a taxi and ask two girls on the street, '*Où est le taxi?*' but they just huddle together and giggle. I walk for a while and a taxi finally stops, and when I show the driver the address he says something under his breath and does a violent U-turn. The man has just farted, deep and spicy. I wind down the window and breathe in the scent of exhaust and smoke and butter as the city swirls about the car in a blur of cement and scarves and bikes and noise. A sign reads *Bastille* and as we circle around a tall green pole with a gold angel on top, I feel stupid for having expected to see a prison.

The hotel has a reception with a piano in it, and a little old lady who is expecting me. She is nice and *ne parle pas anglais* so she speaks loud and slow to me like I'm an idiot. Which I am. The room is cheap, so I pay for a week up front and drag my suitcase up six flights of stairs to a door on a landing, next to a closet with brooms and cleaning supplies. A wet mop leans against the door and I place it gently in a corner. There are no other rooms on the floor except a curtained-off area with a shower hose and a toilet, which consists of a hole with two ceramic imprints either side shaped like feet.

My room is so beautiful, so Parisian, so high up it's quiet. An embroidered white curtain billows out over a single sunken bed. I kneel on it to look over the busy avenue below. People are just tiny blobs with feet poking out of them. Dizzy, I pull my head straight back in and wipe my dusty forearms on my jeans. There is a desk with old carvings in the legs. I place my notebook and the Swiss Army knife on the desk. Perhaps I will buy a little bottle of whiskey, I think to myself. Perhaps I will move in. Perhaps the lady will take a liking to me and agree to let me stay for a hundred francs a month and I'll live here forever, banging the piano and reciting poetry. Perhaps I will die here (of consumption) and nobody will notice; the smell will just fly out the window.

To the left of the desk is a small cracked washbasin. The water that comes out is a light grey. I think of prison and imagine myself out on parole. Then I think of lesbians. I put my soap in the little indent and my toothbrush on the edge, with the mouth part hovering over the bowl so it doesn't touch. As there's no cupboard I leave my clothes in the suitcase.

Except for the Special Dress, which I drape over the end of the bed so the creases can fall out. It never ceases to amaze me what a small ball such a lovely dress can become. I sense that feeling come on, the hot-weather-in-dodgy-hotel-rooms one, so I lie down on the bed and think of truckers and sluts in cheap motels on highways in America and give myself a little orgasm.

Then I go back downstairs. There's a man behind the desk this time, with a wide smile and teeth poking out in all directions.

'*Vos clefs, s'il-vous-plaît mademoiselle.*'

The words are a blur but I understand his hand gesture and give him my keys. We strike up a conversation about sunshine and I catch 'outside' and 'hot' and 'day', and of course I know 'Have a nice evening'.

'*Bonne soirée!*' I say back to him, but the 'r' catches in my throat and I sound like I'm being strangled.

It's still light outside though it's seven pm. The street is crammed with traffic and I wait a long time to cross to a painted patisserie that looks itself edible, and I buy the last croissant. The man smiles; it's not the right time of day for a croissant. I know this, but in Australia it's morning and I'm not quite here yet.

The flaky pastry melts in my mouth. It's like no croissant I've ever eaten. At home we have them on Christmas morning, defrosted from a packet and baked with ham and cheese inside. They generally taste like nothing much, but this one feathers my mouth with butter and sweetness. I savour it as I walk down the tree-lined boulevard, turning onto the rue du Faubourg Saint-Antoine, the street the taxi brought me down. I know it goes all the way back to the Louvre, so I point my body that way and walk and walk, glad I chose to wear the Converse and not the shoes with the little heel.

The rue du Faubourg Saint-Antoine is a feast of clothes shops and cafés, movie theatres and bars, all with tall, cream-coloured or grey apartment blocks above them, reaching to the sky. There are lots of woven wicker chairs like in the movies, but a lot more graffiti. I wander and marvel and drink it all in, beyond delirious now, and as I move through the complete unfamiliarity I start to see familiar things, familiar people – the French version of my brother on a motorbike, the Australian prime minister begging outside a supermarket, Chris in a dark bar, kissing another girl. Mum selling bread. Myself in a cheese-shop window: Hello, French me.

Bon-Jour.

I keep walking. If I stay in a straight line I know I'll be able to find my way back. A sign reads *Internet* so I go in and write a quick email to Mum, telling her I've qrrived and am qlive, because the 'q' on the French keyboard is where the 'a' should be. Back in the street the sun is now low and bright in my eyes, casting the people in front of me in silhouette. I shield my eyes and keep walking, back past the gold angel at Bastille, past a church, a row of fashion shops and a small children's fair, to where the street becomes wider and the shops begin selling berets and snowdomes and posters of old French cabaret shows. Tourists gaze and wrestle maps. I still can't quite see; I bump into a man who says, '*Bonsoir Mademoiselle!*' He is selling last-minute tickets to a play at the Comédie Française, and he is so nice that I buy one. The play is by Tchekhov: *La Cerisaie*, whatever that means. The man points towards the theatre and I walk right past the space octopus and the recent ghost of myself on the backpack in the square. Sorry, *mademoiselle*, can't stop – off to the theatre, *courage!*

Inside, the Comédie Française is a fairytale of gold and red velvet, and I glide up the stairs to the highest floor, where a handsome usher says, '*Bonsoir,*' and lights his little torch. My seat is in the front row of the topmost balcony. I can see just a small part of the stage, so I stand and peer over once and never again. Falling from a balcony in the Comédie Française would be a dumb, if romantic, way to die. The play starts and I can see only the tops of the actors' heads, which eliminates any chance of understanding their words. That's okay; from up here I can almost touch the gold of the proscenium arch, and in this place just below the painted ceiling of swirling clouds and sky, nothing earthly matters anyway.

When the play is over we clap and clap and then everyone starts clapping in time, which gives me a curious feeling and I feel compelled to break the rhythm. There are about eight curtain calls, which seems a bit indulgent, and then, hands tingling, I climb down all the stairs and go and sit in a brasserie and eat three-cheese tagliatelle, because it's the only vegetarian thing I see on the menu. I still can't eat an animal, even a French one. The pasta is rich and salty, and I have a glass of chablis that the *garçon* recommends and am drunk straight away. I suddenly feel self-conscious about being alone and so take out my notebook and try to act like I'm a writer, or a journalist. The *garçon* is very energetic: I write the word 'maniacal' down and try to make words of four letters or more out of it. I am very pleased with 'almanac' and desperately wish I could make 'claimant', but there's no 't', and no point wishing there was.

It must be midnight when I arrive back at the hotel.

'*Vous venez d'où mademoiselle?*' asks the smiling man from earlier, handing me my keys. 'Where you coming from?'

'*Austra-lee,*' I say. 'Australia. Sorry, my French is very bad.'

'No, French *good,*' he says, showing his incredible teeth, of which there aren't many. One is silver, two are gold, and the rest are shades of yellow and grey. '*Comment tu t'appelles?*'

'Jayne. *Tu – comment t'appelles-tu?*'

'Gérard.'

A successful interaction. He '*tu*'d me – the form you use for friends. That's nice. He starts talking fast and I make out a few words and laugh, thinking to myself, Good, this is good practice.

'*On prend un 'tit verre ensemble?*' he says, pulling out two glasses and a bottle of something amber, and I think, Excellent, this is excellent practice, though I'm really woozy now.

'Jeaahhne,' he says, coming out from behind the desk and gesturing towards the little chaise longue next to the piano. He looks out of place in this dainty, feminine setting. Instead of choosing a tapestry chair, he sits next to me on the chaise.

'*Alors* … why you coming in France?'

'Euh, I'm not really certain. Just to learn. You can speak to me in French, I studied it at university. *Je parle Français.*'

So we start a conversation in French, which in retrospect I imagine went something like this:

'Want to sleep in my room tonight?'

'Yes, my room is very nice.'

'Are all Australian girls this beautiful?'

'Yes, Australia is a beautiful country.'

'Australian women are sexy.'

I hear 'sexy' and put two and two together.

'Okay, well, I'm going to bed now, thanks for the drink.'

He stands and offers to accompany me up to my room. 'That's how we do things in this country,' he says before I can object, a serious look on his face. '*La politesse.*'

What can I say?

The walk up the stairs seems to go on forever and I keep thinking, I'm sure it's fine, I'm sure I've just mistranslated the situation, but with each floor the realisation sinks in deeper that there is nobody else in this hotel, no doors slamming, no kids crying, no noise whatsoever in fact, just the floral relief wallpaper becoming more and more yellowed the higher we go, the carpet more and more worn, until the last floor – broom closet open, mop in the corner now dried stiff. The world is silent. Mum says, Silly girl, in my head.

'*Merci, bonne nuit,*' I say, stabbing my key in the lock.

'*Un bisou.*' He puts his hand on the door.

'*Pardon?*'

'Kiss. *Bisou.* This is custom in our country. I drink you. You kiss me.'

'*Non.* No *bisou.*'

He is not smiling now. I try to turn the key but the lock is old and sticky. His hand is damp. My heart pounds.

'*Bisou,*' he says in my ear, but the key has turned and I squeeze backwards through the doorway, slam the door and press my body against it.

'Sweet dream,' he whispers through the keyhole.

There is a long silence in which neither of us moves. Finally, he clomps down the stairs. I grab the Swiss Army knife and flick it open, clutching it close to my chest, my other hand clenched so tight around the lucky penny it cuts into my palm. He has a key. Will he come back? If he does I will stab him. Would I stab him? Yes. Deep in the ribs. No one will know. I can live life on the run.

I prop a chair under the doorknob like they do in movies but it won't stay. The desk won't budge. I stand by the door for what feels like hours, then eventually sit and finally lie on the bed, heart still thumping hard in my chest. Hours go by. Cars. Buses. Motorbikes. Ambulances. There are cracks in the ceiling. A moth in the corner of the room, frozen. Dead or alive? It seems to be staring at me. Is it a French moth or has it too flown here from somewhere far away? I wonder what it is thinking. Idiot, turning up in this city alone with no job, no plans. Shut up, moth. My shoes knock together, *tap tap tap*. If I keep my gaze fixed on the moth, it makes me feel better.

A street sweeper goes by. A pigeon coos outside my window.

I watch the moth. It doesn't move. And I don't move. And it doesn't move.

And the man doesn't come back, except in my mind, in all kinds of ways.

When the sun is up I pack my things. The old lady is at the desk now, and in awkward spurts I try to explain what happened. She gets the gist and goes on an indecipherable rant. I understand 'bastard', 'begs for a job', 'I am kind', 'I am not racist', and 'police'. I'm grateful that she believes me but I don't want to deal with the cops, so I ask for the rest of my money back and leave her railing around her salon like an aproned Rumpelstiltskin.

It's a relief to be at ground level. Lights are still on in the streets. The sky is early-morning blue. Mini trucks sweep the pavements. Men in overalls smoke and drink coffee in the bars. I don't know where to go, so I wander all the way to the Louvre again and on to the Tuileries Garden and sit down on a steel chair near a pond with ducks in it with electric-green necks. The Eiffel Tower spears from the trees. I think about calling Mum and Dad but they will just worry. I think about calling Chris but that would be confusing. There's nothing to do but be here.

As the city comes to life I leave the seat and go inside the Louvre and sit in front of *The Raft of the Medusa* for half an hour. The enormity of it makes me feel insignificant and better. Perspective sorted, I go into the toilets, tame my wild hair and splash my face, which looks tired but alive. Then I leave the building and head towards the Seine.

Room of Good

I read in a novel once that you can find jobs and accommodation at the American Church, and, sure enough, there's the church in my little red book: *Église américaine*. After four days in the youth hostel I decide to try it: I don't want to be a youth anymore, and the sound of two German goths rooting on the bunk above me is about to send me over the edge.

The church is impressive and has toilets you don't have to pay for, so I am already pleased with my mission, though I can't see any board with jobs on it. A kind lady in an oversized knit shows me to a breezeway where all kinds of notices are tacked to a cork board: *Babysitter / Au pair / Chambre libre / Can you teach English?* Maybe I could be an au pair, I think; I like kids. I take down some details, then go and buy a sandwich niçoise with the tuna pulled out of it to take down to the riverbank. The sandwich has a rank, fishy note to it because the woman refused to make me a fresh one *sans* tuna. 'It's not good like that,' she said. Vegetarian is proving difficult. All the more reason to get my own fridge.

The water sparkles in the midday light as I sit on the bank, my view of the river and some interesting boathouses blocked by an attractive couple deep-tonguing each other. I shut Chris out of my mind, throw the remnants of the sandwich in the bin, and go and stand in a smashed-in phone booth with my list. The first voice says something about papers, so I hang up. The next two speak too fast in French, so I hang up. The

14

last entry reads: *Au pair – chambre de bonne – bonnes conditions*. I dial the number slowly.

A little boy giggles as I stammer in French. A man takes the phone and sighs. 'Can you come now?'

⁓

Marcel Florent is a lawyer for Philip Morris. He lives at 41, rue Cardinet, an elegantly understated street in the 17th arrondissement, near the manicured Parc Monceau, with his languid wife, Marie, a psychologist (who smokes Philip Morris); their cherubic four-year-old son, Paul; and their cat-food-ad cat, Ondine. They also have a brusque nanny called Gina, an original Tamara de Lempicka, parquet floors that squeak when you walk on them, balconies that go the whole way around the apartment, and walls high enough to house paintings grand enough for the Louvre. I'm not sure it matters if they like me or not: they seem tired, and, having established that I speak English, hire me on the spot.

Gina takes me through the kitchen into a stairwell and up three flights of rickety stairs to the fifth floor, where there are a lot of brown doors in a row. She points to an open doorway down the hall, turns and leaves. A person's sharp movements are casting shadows against the wall. I approach the door; a buxom blond girl is throwing things into a backpack, muttering swear words in a thick Irish accent. She gives me a foul look before throwing me a key and blowing past in a haze of patchouli. At the end of the hall she turns and says, 'Mind yourself,' and is gone.

I step inside.

I have a home.

Chambre de bonne actually means 'maid's room', but I think it means 'room of good', which makes sense because it *is* good. So good in fact, that the moment I move in the lucky penny simply disappears from the string it was on. I hunt on my hands and knees – nothing – and look for a break in the string. There isn't one. It makes no sense, but I give up searching for a reason. It doesn't matter. I have a home. My very first apartment, if you can call it that; it's really more of a cubby – a simple box with a little square window in a sloping white wall, a floor made of cracked, uneven tiles. I touch everything in it. The mini fridge with a camp stove on top. The damaged Ikea bookshelf. The very ugly and cumbersome desk. The broken floor lamp with its heavy marble base. Mine. Mine. Mine. In the centre of the room is a bed on stilts with a wobbly stepladder and pilled sheets, a lumpy pillow shaped like a sausage. I roll around in it. Then I climb back down. There is a plastic shower cabin over near the window. I pull off my sticky clothes and step into it. My own shower. The free-range hose, I discover, can be pointed in all kinds of pleasing directions.

There's no toilet. The shower is fine for number ones, but for twos there's a cubicle down the hall with a hole in the wall and pigeons roosting in it. It is shared by the dozen or so fifth-floor residents. There's no lock but there is, I learn one night from a hairy man with red underpants around his ankles, a door-slam code. If the door's open it's all yours. If it's closed you must retreat and wait for the sound of the courtesy slam.

The wealthy residents of number 41 are assigned one or two *chambres de bonne* for storage, cleaning supplies, humans. The *chambres de bonne* have their own address: 41bis rue Cardinet. Not to be confused with 41. A *bis* must be an afterthought. An addendum. 41bis has its own modest doorway, mouse-like in comparison to the imposing entrance of number 41 with its carved wooden door and marble foyer; 41bis only half exists, it is just a stairwell with a door on each floor that opens into one of the grand kitchens of number 41. A servant's entrance. On the ground floor lives the *gardienne*, Madame Lechon, who has a little window that opens onto both 41 and 41bis. Whether I'm talking to her from 41 or 41bis, she regards me with contempt, and I start calling her Madame Cochon in my head, which means Mrs Pig, and makes me feel better.

The Burnt Baguette

The first thing I want to do, naturally, after settling into my Room of Good, is go to the boulangerie and buy my first baguette, wearing a headscarf. The one on the corner screams heaven, with its displays of glistening cakes and constant waft of baking bread. I stand in the queue listening earnestly to the people around me, practising in my head the line I've been preparing since high school: *Je voudrais une baguette.* It seems abrupt the way the lady up front says, '*Donnez-moi* (give me),' but her lilting tone makes anything acceptable.

'*Deux croissants s'il-vous-plaît*,' says the suited man now up front.

'*Onze francs soixante-quinze*,' smiles the plump lady behind the counter.

A woman orders a baguette and a mille-feuille. How can she eat pastries and stay so thin?

'*Treize dix-sept*,' smiles the shop lady.

My soul is alight with buttery bakery goodness. The baguettes look so good, I can't wait to make one mine.

'*Mademoiselle?*'

My turn. I smile as warmly as I can, and say in my politest French, '*Bonjour madame, je voudrais une baguette s'il-vous-plaît.*'

She looks at me. Pauses. Then turns to the baguettes lined up behind her. But rather than choosing one of the beauties begging to be picked, she reaches behind the upright basket to pull out an ugly, overcooked one.

'*Quatre francs deux,*' she says nasally, bored.

I'm shocked. Is she serious? I have neither the language skills nor guts to deal with this. All I can do is moronically take the baguette, say *merci*, pay and leave. As I walk down the street clutching my shame, I'm sure people are staring and pointing: 'Ha! Loser! *Vite Benoît!* Come look at burnt baguette girl in the cheap headscarf!'

Back in my room I attempt to break the log against a bedpost, jarring my wrist. If only Dad were here, he loves things overcooked. Great, now I'm homesick.

The incident replays itself over and over in my head. What did I do wrong? How could she be so mean when I was so nice? Tomorrow I'll try harder, I resolve.

Fool.

My extra efforts have no effect, the reverse in fact: the next day my baguette is even worse – it's not even straight – and I have a nagging suspicion they've prepared it specially for me. I try going to the boulangerie at a different time but the afternoon lady is even meaner. I try other boulangeries but encounter similar frostiness and baseball-bat bread. It's clear that my photo is sticky-taped out the back of every bakery in Paris.

In the following weeks I learn that the nicer I am, the nastier the baguette. In fact there seems to be a direct correlation between my friendliness and the baguette's disgustingness.

One day, I've had enough. I awake, throw back the sheets, flex, rehearse my slightly improved vocabulary and march down to the *bread shop* to demand, 'A baguette, please. No, that nice one over there. And no more nonsense, wench.' I didn't say that last part, but if I'd known how to I might have.

The lady stops and beholds me a moment. Then the heavens clear as she breaks into a wide grin. With a great earthy chuckle, she turns in slow motion, and to the tune of 'Dream Weaver' selects the freshest baguette on the rack, wraps it lovingly and hands it to me like a prize. When she says, '*Quatre francs deux*,' she has the voice of an angel.

And so it is. I am in.

This is the Lesson of the Burnt Baguette. Be nice, and eat charcoal the rest of your life.

⟀

'Sorry I'm late,' I say, slamming the door and throwing my bag on the table. Paul sits dwarfed by the marble expanse of the kitchen table, digging at chicken nuggets with a spoon.

He isn't half as bad as my predecessor intimated, though he does try to dominate me in the beginning. I'm his hundredth au pair, he tells me, so I guess that's understandable. The last one, Oonagh, didn't even say goodbye. But I mustn't succumb. The Lesson of the Burnt Baguette helps me to not be too nice. He respects this and soon falls into line.

My job, in exchange for the Room of Good, is to collect him from school each day at four-thirty, take him to the park, give him his dinner, bathe him and put him to bed. I am also to babysit some weekends and evenings. Which turns out to be most weekends and evenings.

'*C'est dégueulasse*,' he scoffs at his plate.

'Disgusting,' I say. I have been grilled about speaking only English with Paul, and making sure he speaks English back.

'Deez-guthing.'

'Are you still hungry?' I ask, scooping the greyish remains into the bin.

'Ess,' he says, 'I am angry.'

'What do you want?'

'Mmm …' He considers, puckering his lips like a middle-aged gourmand. '*Un peu de pâtes*.'

'Pasta,' I correct him. Paul always wants pasta. I make him a bowl of spaghetti and sit down next to him as he slurps it up, lashing his face with red.

'What did you do today?' I ask. He ignores me. I don't even care what he did. I want to be upstairs with the lights off, watching the man who has just moved into the apartment opposite.

Marcel has a late work meeting. Marie sweeps into the kitchen, all perfumed and unzipped, cigarette hanging from her lips as she fiddles with an earring. She is wearing no bra and her breasts are in all directions. I know them well by now.

'*Aidez-moi Jayne chérie.*' Marie speaks no English. She is the only French practice I am getting. In the outside world I mostly stick to English-speaking places – the internet café, the Australian bar, the Shakespeare and Company bookstore, and the park, where I talk to English-speaking nannies. Mum wonders why I don't immerse myself more in the language, but she doesn't know what it's like. People speak so fast, and though my language is improving, especially in boulangeries, I have never felt like such an outsider in all my life. English is the one safe place I can hide.

'Where are you going tonight?' I ask nervously in French, tugging her zip up over her smooth skin. She hasn't mentioned my lateness, though she must have noticed, having thrown Paul the nuggets.

Bruno's opening, she tells me, stubbing out her cigarette in a plate next to Paul's bowl. I love the way she pronounces the vowels in Bruno's name. Brew*noh*. He is Marcel and Marie's favourite contemporary artist. The walls of the kitchen feature two of his Laughing Cow collages, and in the entranceway, next to the Tamara de Lempicka, is a sculpture of a bird he gave Marie for her birthday. My favourite piece is the cigarette lighter he made, which sits in the salon – a little city made of gold, with a tiny arm that takes your cigarette on a Wee Willie Winkie journey through doorways and streets to a burning coil that lights the end before presenting it to you, filter first.

Marie twirls out the door and I put Paul in his pyjamas and read him *Les Ratinos*. I've given up trying to read him English books at bedtime, and he's said he won't tell. He puts his downy head on my lap and says the words, correcting me when I get it wrong.

'You speakin' French very bad,' he says as I turn out the light.

'Thanks a lot,' I say, kissing him goodnight. I go into the salon and curl up on the endless sofa and light cigarette after cigarette on Bruno's city. There's a full moon and I turn off the lights. With the moonlight streaming across the old floors and up the paintings and the sculptures on plinths, the apartment feels like a museum after hours. I go out onto the balcony and smoke amongst the plants, the building opposite dead and dark. My stomach grumbles.

In the kitchen, Marie has left a pus-coloured tin of flageolet beans on the bench for me. On Tuesday it was leftover vegetables that had been served under a dish of tongue. I put the beans back on the shelf and pull out some chocolate biscuits and eat five before returning to the sofa. I stroke Ondine, staring at the moon and trying to feel at home.

Paul squeals: a nightmare. I lead him to the toilet and he pees across the side, pointing his *zizi* at me to wipe up the drips. I cuddle him back to sleep. His hair smells like milk.

Marie stumbles in at two am.

'Jayne ...' she says, falling onto the sofa. Her lipstick is smudged.

'How was the opening?' I ask, heading to the door of the salon.

'So, so good. Bruno, he's so, so good.'

'Paul went straight to sleep, but he had a little nightmare.'

'Paul,' she says, as though she has never heard of him. She holds out her foot to me and pouts her bottom lip. I pull off her shoe. She holds out her hand, wiggling it at me. '*Merci*, Jayne *chérie*,' she says, grasping my hand. 'Stay here tonight, in the guestroom. Can you stay here?'

Marie wishes I'd always sleep in the guestroom – live in the guestroom. It was never intended that I'd live in the Room of Good; the previous au pairs lived here in the apartment and just stored their stuff up there. The guestroom is about four times the size of my place and has a sumptuous king-sized bed, Peter Pan windows, and its own marble bathroom. But though I've tried twice, I can never fall asleep there. It doesn't feel right. I like my room with its shabby bed and medieval key.

Marie has fallen asleep on the sofa. I slip out and up the stairs to my own sweet silence.

Friends

On my days off I experience as much of Paris as I can, scratching my name in the top of the Eiffel Tower, spending entire days in the Louvre, the Palais de Tokyo, Sacré-Coeur, Musée Rodin, Musée d'Orsay. I go to plays and watch movies with no English subtitles. But having nobody to share it with, or to even see me doing these things, makes it feel like none of it's happened. I spend time with some of the English nannies in the park, and in internet cafés writing home. But more and more I'm happiest to be in my Room of Good.

From my little square window I have a storybook view of the expansive fourth-floor apartment across the street, with its floor-to-ceiling windows/doors and ancient chandeliers. The apartment is just far enough away that I can't make out the exact features of the man who lives inside, but I can see that he has dark hair and moves with the purpose of someone who is not too young, though his slim build tells me he is not too old either. His shirts are loose and he wears pants and bare feet, which I can see when he comes out to lean over the balcony and smoke, peering down at the street.

Whatever his age, he seems too young for the apartment, with its ornate plant pots and opulent curtains, which makes me think it belongs to his parents, or perhaps his grandmother, and he's using it for a time. Is he American, here for the summer? No, definitely French – too much smoking, too-skinny ankles. Maybe his family have places all over the country, and in New York too. There's something aristocratic about the arrangement. He is a prince, perhaps – a modern-day prince who wants to live a normal life, fleeing the oppression of the castle to be in Paris amongst the people. To work.

And he does work, but I can't figure out what he does. Banker, I thought at first, because of the wealth and attire, but a banker wouldn't hunch over his desk the way he does, wouldn't stare out the window or walk from room to room with his hands clasped above his head. A writer, then. But he works by hand in what looks like a leather-bound folio, which he folds up and carries under his arm. Could he be sketching? No, someone who draws wouldn't gaze so long out into nothingness. Could he be an actor, learning his lines? Making notes? It's possible. But I don't see him pacing, mouthing words, gesturing. No, he's thinking. He must be a writer. A writer who writes by hand and who has already written something important, given the array of slender women I have watched coming and going from his bed, gliding out in his shirts to look over the street, a different kind of thought on their faces. What *is* he writing?

Out in the world I see many versions of him – Corporate Prince, Bartender Prince, Métro Prince, each with the same outline but different faces. One day in the mini supermarket down the street I think I see the real him, but there is no leather-bound folio to confirm it. What would I say anyway? 'Hi, I'm your neighbour, I watch you from across the street; what are you writing?' Perhaps he would smile and ask me to come over and put on one of his shirts, make love to me like Vincent Perez, then let me sleep as he smoked and mused by the large pot plant, savouring the new inspiration he'd found in me for his next poem.

But I know this would never happen. If I approached him I would be breaking an important code. Here, people in windows don't exist. It's a contract. I learnt this from Smoking Man. Every morning, a fat naked man leans over his ornate second-floor balcony, a few floors below the Prince, smoking. He is middle-aged, with a thick head of grey-black hair and a belly so large that I can't see his penis; even if I'm watching from the Florents' windows, which I am often. Smoking Man is dashing despite his weight – probably a judge. He knows the rules. Life is to be enjoyed. Who cares about the little boy and his au pair giggling behind the curtains across the way? Smoking Man owns the code.

It's comforting in some way: I'm alone and yet not. I have the Prince, Smoking Man, and the characters in Marcel's English library, which consists entirely of Bret Easton Ellis novels. Patrick Bateman is proving an exceptional pal, especially on pages 162 to 169, which are becoming exposingly dog-eared. Plus I have the cockroaches. One day an entire community moves in and sets up. They're small and brown, not the big black nuclear-holocaust survivors of home. At first I tried smashing them with footwear, but quickly gave up: the more I tried, the more determined they were to stay. My disgust turned to respect – their resolve was inspiring – and they soon ceased to bother me at all. On nights when it's too hot to sleep up on the bed, they show their reciprocal respect by not climbing on me as I starfish on the floor, making tracks around my body instead, like chalk marks at a crime scene.

After putting Paul to sleep one night, I'm walking towards the kitchen door when Marcel calls out from the salon.

'Jayne! Do you like *Blackadder*?'

The last thing I want to do after a long day of babysitting is hang with Marcel, but the TV is loud and colourful and my Room of Good has recently become unbearably quiet.

He is sitting on the floor, leg bent up to his crotch, shoes off, mauve socks on, a cigarette in one hand, a glass of amber liquid in the other. Rowan Atkinson is abusing Baldrick. Marcel gestures towards the vacant sofa.

'Where's Marie?' I ask.

'Out with friends. Can I get you a drink?' He goes into the dining room and comes back with a heavy crystal tumbler with a thick band of liquid in it. 'Try this. Ice?'

'No thanks.'

'Correct answer. It's fine alcohol, I wouldn't have let you. Taste.'

It is pear-flavoured, strong and smooth but prickly on my tongue. I allow a tiny amount to linger and spread before taking another sip. I'm not sure how to sit.

'This series is my favourite,' he says.

'Yeah, I haven't seen them all. But I love Queenie.'

'Me too.' We chuckle our way through several episodes, Marcel changing my liqueur at the end of each to something more exquisite and rich.

'So, what do you do with your life?' he asks after episode three. 'What is your *deal*?'

The line makes me cringe – or perhaps it's the way his seam cuts into his nuts as he eases forward in his pants.

'I'm not sure yet. I think I want to be an actor. Or maybe a painter. Or a director or something.'

'Ooh, that's tough, the arts.' Marcel makes a dismissive hand gesture. 'No money. Always a struggle for the money. Don't you want money?'

'Yes, but, I don't know. I want to do something I like.'

'But how will you survive? You want to be an au pair your whole life?'

'No, but —'

'You must find the money. I am happy. Work – *bof* – but I have the money. My parents they always say that to me. They send me to a private school when I was ten, like Paul will go to school, and after I studied law and now I make a lot of money. It is good. But it will be difficult, maybe impossible, for you to make money as an artist. Unless you are very good of course. Are you good?'

'I don't know yet.'

'You need to be very good to make money in your business.'

He gets up, brings me another drink and puts on episode six.

I wake surrounded by a delectable softness, not knowing where I am. It's dawn. I look around and realise I'm in the guestroom bed. Top off. Jeans on.

Out the window I can see Smoking Man on his balcony, nude as ever. He seems to be looking at me, though I'm sure he can't see in. He's smiling.

I pull on my top and shudder. I can't remember how the night ended. Did I just come in here and pass out?

The air is cool in the morning light. I step lightly on the bits of the parquet I know don't make any noise and climb the dusty stairwell up to the Room of Good.

⁓

Marcel and Marie and Paul are moving to Switzerland. They are selling both 41 and 41bis, and I will have to move. My return ticket was booked for a week from today, and although I had been toying with the idea of staying I decide to use it. Paul is devastated. There is really no other option – my tourist visa only allows me to stay three months and I'm about to run out of money. What would I do? How would I work? Where would I live?

My last days are a kind of purgatory.

I walk aimlessly through the streets, ignoring signs, forgetting my guidebook. I get on and off the métro at random stations, wandering around and looking at things and letting myself get lost. I pack up my Room of Good. I take Paul to the park and buy him as many ice-creams as he wants. I stand in front of as many famous artworks as I can, and will them to go into me.

On my second-last day I arrive at a beautiful church somewhere on the Left Bank. Saint-Sulpice. The outside is covered in scaffolding and I work my way past it, through a group of tourists and down towards the back, where I discover a shrine of Mary. I close my eyes and feel nothing.

Outside, the glow of sunset is still bright. Dusk seems to last forever here. I wander the streets, losing all sense of where I am, following things that attract my eye: a strange window mannequin here, a bizarre sculpture there, a shop selling only belt buckles. I stop outside a mesmerising patisserie and stand for a long time admiring the delicate pastel colours and immaculate shapes and textures. I'm always afraid to go into such beautiful shops – what if I change my mind and don't want anything, or I can't afford anything? I find myself walking in.

I buy a *religieuse*. I have wanted to buy a *religieuse* since I was twelve and saw a picture of one in a textbook. A round puff full of cream, with another, smaller puff of cream on top, each covered in chocolate frosting. A lady dressed in sugar-pink builds a little paper tent around it and hands it to me in a carefully outstretched palm.

The cake is hard to walk with, especially as I approach the river, where the foot traffic increases. I hold the fragile pyramid upright in my palm, trying to avoid people bumping into it. I focus hard as I weave in and out, wanting to bite into it then and there, but it demands space and time and stillness. The crowd thins as I cross a bridge behind Notre-Dame and head down towards the riverbank. People are talking, kissing and licking ice-creams on the stone embankment, and I find a place as far away from everyone as I can, near an old man fishing. He doesn't acknowledge me as I sit down and place the precious object on the wall beside me while I swing my legs around to a view of the booksellers and wonky buildings on the opposite bank. I'm not quite sure where I am – on the Right Bank, the Left Bank, or an island. I think of pulling out my red book but it doesn't matter.

The sky clouds over as I open the package and admire the *religieuse*. Its edges gleam. Does the name mean angel? Nun? Priest? I bite off its head. Chocolate cream mixes with the pillowy pastry and sweet buttery frosting. Oh, heaven. My head floats. Perhaps it's called a *religieuse* because eating it is a religious experience. I allow the sensation to last in my mouth as long as I can before putting more in.

A pigeon lands next to the fisherman's boot. His line stretches. Nothing.

A woman in heels passes behind me.

'*Mademoiselle?*'

My scarf has fallen. I thank her and stuff it into my bag.

The priest is almost entirely in me now. Tourist boats go by, I wave. A couple on the opposite bank share a bottle of wine, legs kicking out over the river wall. The fisherman's line creates a tiny ripple in the water. As I finish the last morsel, the clouds clear away. I look down the river and take in the entire view, the sky and the river, the rooftops and chimneys and boats. And in that moment something happens.

I see the view. Really *see* it. I've witnessed landscapes like this before in Paris, I know they're beautiful, but for the first time it seems to exist within me. It doesn't matter that nobody is here to see it with me, I don't need anyone else to make it real. It *is* real.

My breath catches in my chest. The sweetness of the *religieuse* pounds through my veins. An involuntary squeak comes out and the fisherman looks over at me, then, nonplussed, back to his rod.

La Femme Nikita

Instead of returning to Melbourne with a stronger sense of self, I am more amoeba-like than ever. I move back into my parents' place, into my old bedroom, and curl up on my mother like a baby pup. I've never been less sure what to do with my life. Paris has disoriented me, and I am paying for having chosen the vaguest subjects I could at university: a double degree in criminology and French was never going to lead very far.

'Maybe you can work with French-speaking criminals,' says Dad.

'Thanks, Dad.'

One morning, flipping through the jobs section, I see an ad for someone with two specific qualifications: a degree in a foreign language and a degree in law or criminology. The job? Intelligence Officer for ASIO – the Australian Security Intelligence Organisation. In other words: spy.

This is very cool. I set about preparing my application, to my sister's laughter:

'You don't want to be a spy. You just want to wear the outfits.'

I'm offended. Then I realise it's true. If I close my eyes I see myself as La Femme Nikita, rolling across floors with a gun, in a miniskirt. Then and there, I commit myself to the pursuit of acting. I audition for drama school and am accepted. For the next three years I study

Shakespeare and Tchekhov and the contemporary greats, learning vocal technique and improvisation. I graduate with flying colours, secure an agent, and am full of hope and excitement about my impending career. I will act in the theatre, in television, be popular, successful; I'll appear on the front cover of magazines with my hand on my chin.

Nothing could have prepared me for the post-school silence. Waiting for the phone to ring, going from audition to audition only to be told I'm too this and not enough that. Gabriella, my best friend from drama school and a similar 'type' to me, gets called for the same auditions, leading to a weird, competitive dynamic between us. I don't like the feeling of scrabbling for roles and I don't like the cameras in cold rooms with people in suits. I begin to dream about taking off to Paris again, to attend Lecoq, the theatre school I'd read about where they teach you not just to act, but to make your own work. Acting is fun, but if you're not cast you can't just do it anyway, unlike playing a guitar or writing a book or painting a canvas.

I want to make my own work, but I have no idea how. The Lecoq school costs more for a term than I make from my part-time jobs in a year, and that's without considering flights and living costs. My only choice is to consider a second career, and take whatever acting jobs I can get on the side.

In university I played old Miss Prism in a French production of *The Importance of Being Earnest*. As fewer actors spoke French, I had more chance of getting fun roles, even if they didn't suit my age or type at all. That company is holding auditions for the role of Elvire, the wife in Molière's *Dom Juan*. I get the part.

I'm Sorry,
We Still Have Time

One day in dress rehearsal for the Molière production, I'm having my bodice stitched up when my phone rings. It's Dad.

'Can you come home please?' he says. His voice is strange.

'Sure, I'll see you after rehearsal.'

'No, I need you to come now.'

'I can't, Dad, it's dress.'

'Sorry, but you have to come now. It's important.'

I don't ask what's wrong. I hang up and tell the director I have to leave, and go straight to the car. My hands tremble on the wheel. I light a cigarette. Norma, my 1960s Cortina, is too old to go on the tollway and I don't have one of those electric passes but I rattle along it anyway, eyes blankly monitoring the temperature gauge. The trip out to the suburbs lasts hours and a split second at the same time. I flash back to the hospital, the tests; my mother sitting on the bed with the tape across her voice box, the redheaded male doctor.

'It's just an annoying condition I'll have to take medication for,' she said. 'It's called sarcoidosis. Nothing to worry about.' The word sounded so awful, all I could think of were hot coils in her throat, but she assured me it really was nothing.

When I pull up outside the house it looks as it always does. The curtains are open. A kid whooshes by on a skateboard. I mount the steps to the only home our family has had.

Dad is in the kitchen making tea, his back turned. The kitchen looks the same, the cork floor, the fridge covered in stickers and magnets, the hum of the dishwasher. Mum's handbag on the kitchen counter, with all its mystery. Dad keeps jiggling his teabag. 'We're just waiting on Kate.' He leaves the room without me seeing his face.

There are no biscuits in the pantry and no chocolate in the cupboard above the microwave. I'm not hungry anyway. I stand at the window and watch my brothers shoot hoops. The dog runs around their ankles. The strong smell of the gardenia in a vase above the sink infiltrates my nose, tightening my stomach.

Kate walks in, banging the back door. Beautiful Kate, so dark, like Mum. The opposite of the boys, me and Dad, all honorary Swedes. She and I share an apartment now, in the city. When the boys finish school, we joke, they can live there too.

Kate raises her eyebrows at me. I shrug. She puts her bag down. The boys come in, puffing. Ben says, 'What do you think's going on?' Kate says no idea. Alex slumps in a chair. My stomach churns.

Dad comes back. His face is frightening. 'Come into the living room,' he says in a small, tight voice. He pulls the couches closer together, into a weird sort of circle. We sit down and Mum enters. Her eyes are red and she looks pale.

'Hi guys.' She smiles and scratches her head. She doesn't hug us. She can't quite look at us. The little piece of blue tape is still on her neck.

She sits down in the armchair she and Dad recently had reupholstered in a contemporary floral pattern. She seems dwarfed by both the chair and the design. Why couldn't they have just kept the green velvet? Dad sits down on his knees, placing his hands on each thigh. He looks like a little boy. He goes to speak, then begins to cry.

I feel like vomiting. We wriggle, it's unbearable, he takes forever to speak. Finally, he manages to spurt, 'We asked you to come because. Basically. Your mother's not well at all. They were wrong.'

33

My hands are tight between my knees. Dad cries more. Then he breathes. As if he's been winded he says, 'It's not sarcoidosis. It's cancer.'

I look at him, waiting for him to say something that will annul what he's just said. His shoulders are hunched and tears drip onto his hands.

I look at Mum. She is even smaller in her chair. It's like she's on trial. I look back at Dad. Go on, I plead silently, go on. Make it go away.

But he doesn't say anything. Kate leans her face into her hands. Ben curls in on himself. Alex sits rod-still. Dad tries to slow his breath in order to speak.

'Lung cancer. And … it's not possible. To operate.'

Our cardboard house falls gently down on us. Dad cries on the carpet. Mum shrinks still further into the chair. Had I really grown up in this house? Did I used to play in that sandpit outside, make Barbie homes inside that cubbyhouse? Who are these people? That is not my dad sitting there, I have never seen this person before. He is a little boy who got lost on his way to the shopping centre. Why won't the little boy stop crying?

Mum's hand is on the arm of the chair. I am close to her but I don't know how to reach out and touch her.

I want to go back. I want to reverse out of the house, go back up Eastleigh Drive, back to rehearsals and do my Act II monologue. I want it to be yesterday, I want to be back in the Greek restaurant, on the funny date with the actor guy, Jack. I want to be in the apartment with Kate, watching her make me a sandwich as I tell her about the date. I want today not to come, I want it not to be now; I want to be a kid again, a snot-nosed toddler, a baby, in her arms, on her chest. I want to crawl back inside her and never be born.

Time has a new texture. Space too. We are far from each other and far from the rest of the world. This tight-knit family, exploded. Mum feels guilty, I can see it. She is leaving us. We don't want her to leave. We would rather anyone else leave. Not her. Why her? She does nothing but help other people. She brings babies into the world! Looks after mothers. Researches how to make their lives better. Looks after us. Looks after everyone. It can't be her. It can't be real.

At some indefinable point she turns to us and says, 'I'm sorry. We still have time.'

We have thirteen months.

I never thought she would actually die, though the redheaded doctor said, point-blank, 'Six months to two years.' Little grief by little grief, you get lulled into a new reality. First, the news. Grieve that. But she's still there, still looks so well, you'd never know anything was wrong. So you stop grieving. You stay in the present. Chemo. Tubes and needles. Grieve that. But she laughs, her hair stays in, maybe a cure will come. She gets tired. Sleeps until afternoon. Grieve that. But she still laughs, still hugs, still asks all kinds of questions about your new boyfriend Jack. She's still right here. How can there be any grief?

Then the hospital. The I-don't-think-she-can-go-on-like-this-much-longers. The wheezing and gasping, the sprawling red bruise across her back, like two big red wings. Morphine. Palliative care. She sees portals in insipid hospital prints of country England. Talks to her dad in the portals. But she is still warm, still beautiful, still speaks small sentences. And so the plateaux go on, deeper and deeper, until she is in a bed, pillow covered in hair, in and out of consciousness, people shaking their heads a lot. Her eyes open a crack, for you. She squeezes your hand. She is still alive. Your mother. She is right there.

Kate and I are eating ice-creams outside our apartment one hot night with Jack. Our windows are open upstairs and we hear our landline ring. Nobody ever calls the landline. Kate goes up and answers it. Jack and I wait in silence. She comes running back down the stairs. Without speaking, Jack drives us to the hospital. Kate and I sit in the back holding hands like children.

We leave Jack's car. The sliding doors open. A lady is there waiting for us.

'I'm so sorry,' she says. 'You've just missed her.'

Like she's left on a train.

When I was little I would stand by my parents' bed in the deep of night whispering, 'Mum. Mum. Mum.' Eventually she would wake and let me in. 'Five minutes, then back to bed.' I would lie there, stiff as a board, as far away from her as I could get, hoping she would forget I was there. But I could still feel her warmth.

Now I whisper, 'Mum. Mum. Mum.'

She will wake any moment and say, 'What is it, Jaynie?'

My French professor went missing once; there was a newspaper article saying he had *disparu*. Disappeared. I kept waiting for him to come back. I learnt much later that the word actually means 'dead'. The meaning of this was not fully apparent to me until the days and weeks after that strange and silent night. I kept looking for her, expecting to feel her, smell her. But she had disappeared. No matter how hard I tried, how good I was, I would never see her or hear her or smell her again. Her absence was tangible, a hole, sucking all the warmth from the planet.

Months pass. The world feels warped – everything is familiar and yet not. I'm angry at it for being the same, when nothing is, or ever will be again. How can the streets have the gall to look as they did before, the houses, the faces, my front door?

You are Going to Paris

My hair is done, my clothes are neat, and when my heart slows down a bit I'll put on eyeliner and ride to the audition for the insurance commercial. If I get it, that's three months' rent, maybe more. But my heart won't slow down, it keeps speeding up, until it's beating so hard I have to throw myself on the bed before I faint.

This has happened before, and lying flat always helps, but not this time. The thought of fainting while lying down fills me with a new level of dread. My body sinks lower and lower into the bed until it seems to fall right through, down through the floor and the apartment below, into the foundations and dirt, to a cold, cold place. Here in its silent grave my body stops fighting. I relax into the peace of nothingness, relieved, dead. God, it feels good to be dead.

I stay like that for a long time, until air begins to creep back into my nostrils and out of my mouth and I gradually rematerialise on my bed. Still here. I kick off my shoes and crawl under the covers, arms stiff at my sides. Tears spill down my cheeks, though I'm not crying – they do that now of their own volition, like incontinence. Face incontinence. I have no idea how much time passes: all I know is I'm now very late for the audition, and the thought sends me into another state of panic so intense I have to put my knees up and my wrists over my eyes and order myself to breathe, breathe, breathe. The suffocating feeling eventually subsides enough for me to roll over and pick up my phone.

My agent's assistant, Robin, answers. 'Don't worry,' she says, 'I'll let them know.'

Robin took me for a cup of tea when an episode like this, but milder, happened in her office. Her mother died too, she told me, when Robin was in her late forties. She told me age makes no difference, but that twenty-eight was young to lose your mother. 'It doesn't go away, but it does get better,' she said. She also said she'd found a sort of new mother figure in the warmth and wisdom of other women around her. The last thing she said had stuck in my mind: having a mother is like being a balloon tied to the earth. Once she is gone, the string is cut, leaving you to roam untethered forever. 'Which isn't always bad,' she said, patting my arm. 'You'll see.'

I hang up and fall into a heavy sleep. When I wake, it feels past lunchtime, judging by the sun on the palm tree outside. Two birds are chatting on a wire. Of course it's a beautiful day. Australia never has any empathy for your mood.

When will things feel normal again? How to proceed when I don't even have the ability to perform basic tasks like getting out my front door? I need to call Mum to ask her advice on how to get over the death of herself. She would know what to say. 'Eat something. Go for a jog. Come on, Jaynie.'

The image of her drawing murky broth through a straw in a desperate bid to cling to a few more minutes of life wills me into the kitchen. What she'd have done for one more day. One more hour.

Kate has left two crusts of a loaf in a plastic bag and there's an open jar of peanut butter on the bench. She dreams of Mum. For me, her absence is as cold as concrete, even in my sleep. I smear peanut butter on the crusts when they shimmy out of the toaster and sit looking at them. The window is open but the world outside is silent. Everyone's at work, going about their day, smiling, chatting, eating stuff. All I want to do is stop. Forever. Disappear. I know how I'd do it. But the thought of standing is too much, let alone finding my keys. Too lazy even to suicide.

On the table is a scrap of paper with the words *Reiki John* written on it, and a number, which I must have absent-mindedly transcribed when someone said, yet again, with concern, 'I know this guy. He can help.' Who can help with something like this? It's *normal*. People die. It happens every day.

What right have I to be helped anyway? I don't deserve help. I'm a grown woman with a whole life ahead to look forward to. What about Dad? What about people whose parents die when they're little? What about the stolen generations? What about kids in Africa?

Besides, I've already tried two people for help – a trainee counsellor who checked his manual and told me that this kind of grief takes six to twelve months to recover from, and Mum's reiki lady, Magdalena. Mum was a pragmatist and didn't go for hippie stuff, but a friend had recommended Magdalena to her when she fell ill, and she told me the reiki sessions made her feel so calm and well. The Christmas before she died, Mum gave me a voucher to see Magdalena – 'It's your kind of thing, Jaynie!' – and a week after she died I remembered the voucher and went to see Magdalena, thinking it might uncover some secret to Mum I didn't know. The idea of her private world fascinated me: she had never really shown us any of her vulnerability, cancer or otherwise. Had she told Magdalena if she was scared of dying?

Magdalena was just as I imagined: long wavy hair, long dress, beads. She took my rigid body in her arms; she loved my mother dearly, she said. And after lying on the table and having her warm hands hovering near me, I did feel slightly calmer. But that calm disappeared when Magdalena insisted that Mum had come in while I had my eyes shut, and had given me a kiss on the forehead. I wanted to shatter every crystal in her zen den. Even if I believed in anything like that, Mum had left the most tangible stillness I had ever known. Even if she could, she wouldn't have hung around to give kisses on foreheads. She was gone; nothing, no one, had ever been so gone.

But reiki is all the rage right now, and in my circle of friends it's the go-to solution for all life's woes.

On this day, it doesn't matter anymore whether I see Reiki John or not, nothing could make me feel worse, so I decide to call him. Besides, if one more person tells me to see him, I actually will kill myself.

The receptionist says he's had a cancellation and I can come at three. The feeling of having an appointment makes me feel something that is neither good nor bad. Just something.

Reiki John works from a room in a little place built into the stone bridge that goes over the railway tracks to the Ripponlea railway station. The station is at the end of my street, and I must have passed his place a thousand times but I've never noticed it. It's like a troll's home, a cobbled brick wall with tiny windows in it, utterly out of place and yet perfectly belonging. Inside are four practitioners – an osteopath, a masseuse, a counsellor, and John, a 'reiki and spiritual healing practitioner', according to his signage. I sit for ten minutes in the waiting room, staring at an ad for water purifiers, trying to ignore the fact that an actor who graduated from my drama school the year before me (and got a big part in a hit TV series) is sitting opposite, trying also to ignore that she has noticed me.

'Jayne?' The portly receptionist directs me to the end of the hallway, into a warm, darkened room. Reiki John is seated on a comfortable-looking chair next to a small desk. His hands are clasped and he smiles at me, gesturing for me to sit down. He seems ageless – he could be my age, with his waxy skin and fair curls, but his eyes and body have an unwavering quality that makes him seem older. The quietness in his body unsettles me, and I would fidget and chew at the inside of my mouth were I not in such a rock-bottom state.

I slump in the chair like an old curmudgeon, beyond caring.

'So, Jayne, tell me what's been happening in your life.'

I have nothing to lose, so I tell him. Everything. About Mum, about us trying to go on like nothing has happened, about the guilt, the exhaustion, the desire for oblivion. Trying to mother my brothers and sister, their repulsion. How bullshit reiki is. Magdalena's bullshit.

How bullshit everything is. About how my heart seems to have died but I don't have the guts to tell Jack, or the decency to let him go. My selfishness, weakness, how so many people in the world have it so bad. How I've fantasised about moving into a convent, or prison even, somewhere I could hide away and not exist anymore. Death, Paris, the Lecoq school —

'Paris?' he interrupts.

Weeks ago, on a whim, I'd asked the director of the French theatre for a contact at the embassy, and emailed them to ask about scholarships. I heard nothing back. Paris felt further away than death itself.

'You are going to Paris,' he says, before I tell him any of this.

'Yeah right. I have no money, and I don't know how I'd —'

'You're going,' he repeats, face still as ever. 'When you said the word "Paris", your guides came rushing up around your head saying, "Yes! Yes! Yes!" You are going to Paris. I have no doubt about it.'

Reiki John is on crack.

'Now, I'll just get you to take off your shoes and socks and lie up here.'

The room smells like a faraway land. He puts a warm rug over me. The distant sound of harps is interrupted by the rushing of a train.

'Close your eyes and try to relax,' he says. 'I'll be back in a moment.'

Just go with it, I tell myself.

When he returns he stands with his hands hovering above my head for a very, very long time. More trains go by. The string music changes to pipes, then flutes, then piano. Someone else comes quietly into the room, perhaps Reiki John's assistant. They stand together near my head and then they move down towards my right shoulder. Both have their hands hovering over my arm; hers are smaller than his, but just as warm. I feel like opening my eyes to see what the assistant looks like but my lids are too heavy. The two of them stand for a while by my legs, then move down to my feet, staying there for a long time, his hands over my left foot, hers over my right. Hers tremble a bit and feel light and youthful; I have the sense that she's giggly. They swap sides. It's odd, her presence in the room keeps changing. I can almost feel her giggling now. I imagine she has long blond hair. They keep moving around and arrive back at my shoulder. Then the strangest thing happens. I feel the girl lean in, right over me, and for some unknown reason I know it's Mum. She puts her hand on my chest and says three things. I love you. I'm proud of you. You're doing good.

And then everything is quiet.

Reiki John leaves the room. I don't want to open my eyes. I lie for a long time waiting to see if the Mum-girl will come back. Come back!

The door opens and Reiki John taps me on the shoulder. His eyes are wide as I open my own.

'Stay there a moment,' he says.

Face incontinence washes my cheeks.

'I know!' he says. 'Honestly, I think she did come to you at Magdalena's, but you weren't ready. This time she took a form you wouldn't be scared of, perhaps someone a bit like you. And when she was able to get close she passed on her message.'

The fact that Reiki John had felt it without me mentioning it makes me deeply curious. But more than anything, I feel relieved. Those were the exact three sentences I needed to hear. I hadn't known how much I'd needed to hear them.

I walk back up Maryville Street feeling that a great weight has lifted from my shoulders. Kate looks at me strangely as I recount the story – I am desperate that she see John herself and receive her own message. But she isn't interested. She has her dreams. I want Dad to go too, but he just laughs. 'So glad that happened for you, Jaynie.'

A week later I rush back to Reiki John, excited at the thought of seeing Mum again. She doesn't come, but afterwards he tells me she's given him a message. 'She told me to tell you she's fine, and not to worry. And that she's working with the light.'

This makes me happy, though I'm sure he made it up.

Nothing happens the next time I see him either, and I realise I don't need to go again. I am done. Things feel better. I am on the other side. Of course I know it was just my deepest psyche coming up to rescue me. Whatever it is, I don't care. I don't feel the urge to die anymore. I feel like eating things.

A few weeks later, I receive an email from the French embassy in Canberra saying that I'm being considered for a two-year government grant to attend the Jacques Lecoq International Theatre School. This includes payment of the school fees, a monthly allowance, and accommodation at the Centre des Récollets, an ancient monastery close to the school that has been recently restored as a residence for international artists and scientists. Will I please fill in the attached form.

I'm sure I'm dreaming.

But four months later, I'm on a plane to Paris.

Everything Moves

I think I've been scammed. The address for the Jacques Lecoq school is clearly printed on my letter as 57, rue du Faubourg-Saint-Denis, Paris 75010. But where's the old boxing hall from his book *The Moving Body* that I've gazed at for so long? Where's the grand brick façade, the gabled rooftops, the tall windows and skylights? This is just a blue-painted door beneath a shabby, pollution-stained building in the weirdest, wildest Paris street I've ever walked down.

My head spins. Where am I? Through the gaps in the door all I can see is a narrow pathway between two apartment blocks. The street thumps and whirrs behind me. As I take a step backwards I notice beside the door a small plaque that reads *École Internationale de Théâtre Jacques Lecoq*.

This *is* it.

Beside the sign is a keypad. On my letter is a code. I punch it in and the door clicks open. I follow the pathway past the letterboxes and pot plants to a doorway right down the back that stands ajar. It's quiet here, as though the noise and bustle of the street were just in my mind. I push open the door and enter a room with a chequered floor and a wall plastered in colourful theatre posters. Good sign. The chequered floor leads to a narrow corridor, which I follow until I reach a small foyer. A lady in a neat suit and a tight bun is sitting behind a desk.

'*Bienvenüe,*' she smiles at me. 'You are here for the enrolment?'

I hand her my paper and she smiles again. 'Hello Jayne. *Venez.*'

I follow her through a door and down a corridor with worn linoleum floors to a large foyer with lots of doors and a staircase coming from it.

'Madame Lecoq is running a little late. Please wait here,' says the lady, leaving me in the centre of the room.

There are photos on the walls of actors in masks, doing acrobatics, wearing red noses and strange padded costumes. On one wall is an oversized photo of Jacques Lecoq in a black leotard, thrusting his body forward in a lunging pose, his young face calm and serious. *Tout bouge,* he said. Everything moves. What about corpses? I wondered when I read his book. There is a particular stillness to a corpse. I would have liked to ask him the question but he has been dead five years now, his disciples carrying on his teaching in what some say is an even more powerful and essentialised way.

'Jayne?' calls a woman's voice from upstairs. I walk up and up the old wood stairs, drinking in the ancient smell, to arrive at a very high wraparound balcony looking down over a vast room – the one from my book! The vaulted ceilings and industrial lamps hanging from ropes, the iconic round window, the skylights. *La Grande Salle.* The Big Room. In the early 1900s it was a popular boxing ring where Édith Piaf would come and watch her boyfriend. From where I'm sitting I can imagine looking down on two beefcakes pounding it out to the shouts and slurs of the crowd. It makes sense that in the 1970s Lecoq found it the perfect place for his school, not only because of his love for sport, but because of its wide, wooden floors, high ceilings and upstairs viewing gallery.

A small group of people wearing black leotards are moving around in the space below, stopping suddenly and throwing their arms up in the air, bringing them back down to their sides, then doing it all over again. A muscly Asian man calls directions to them, shouting, clapping.

'Jayne?' calls the voice again. Madame Lecoq, Jacques' wife, is a statuesque woman in her seventies with cropped grey hair and painted lips. She speaks perfect English because she is English. She asks me to fill in some forms, and I linger over the question 'mother's occupation'. Am I reading it right? What should I put? Midwife? Disappeared? Light-worker?

'Don't worry about those, they're not important,' she says, too busy to put up with my pause.

She asks how I got the grant and I don't know what to say – it seemed to fall from the sky. I tell her about the French theatre company in Melbourne and the embassy and how it just sort of happened.

'Well, your fees are taken care of,' she says. 'How long do you intend to study here?'

'For the two years,' I say. 'At least, that's what I hope.'

'You will need to work very hard,' she says, voice grim. 'Having a scholarship doesn't guarantee you'll be allowed to complete the entire course. We only take thirty out of the hundred students through to second year.'

I nod, biting the inside of my mouth.

'I hope you feel strong,' she says.

I don't.

                ~

I step tentatively back out into the rue du Faubourg-Saint-Denis. The street is another planet – a far cry from the clean, ordered Paris I knew before. A thousand worlds, each with its own colour and smell and sound, bash up against each other in a crazy harmony: African hair salons next to Middle Eastern delicatessens next to Indian dress shops and Chinese grocery stores and old French brasseries and old-man bars and run-down *tabacs* and pharmacies and gypsy jewellers and supermarkets and flower shops and tribal instrument shops … Turkish, Indian, Italian, Czech – with every step a different culture; happy people, sad people, eating, shouting, singing, shopping and smoking together, the footpaths jammed with tables and chairs and bikes, the road a steady, bumping mess of scooters and cars and vans and trucks and animals. The air is thick with exhaust and curry and cream and tobacco and cheese and barbecued meat and fresh fish and spiced bread, the fragrant fumes of a hookah pipe, the stench of a sewer. Cars honk, bikes ding, people laugh, a homeless man cries into a can of Despérados. A teenage boy in dusty clothes sells ripped DVDs on a rug. A six-foot model sashays past and through a doorway into a hidden courtyard atelier.

The mismatched buildings above the shopfronts – some dilapidated, some renovated – seem to lean over the street as if to observe the flurry, curious but exhausted by the never-ending buzz. The buildings are rough, smooth, crafted, golden, graffitied, filthy, pristine. Men in suits, men at tables, a man outside a halal butcher with a stump for a leg. Cigarette butts and balls of hair blowing in the drains. Overflowing bins. Dogs under tables, cats in windows. I make my way through it all to the top of the street, past the imposing Gare de l'Est to the beautiful white monastery with its belltower and arcades. The Récollets. After five days it already feels like home.

A group of acrobats are rehearsing on the front lawn, shouting to each other, in Portuguese, I think. The building behind them is so beautiful I'm still in shock that I get to live here. The Récollets were a group of Franciscan monks who wore grey pointed hoods and devoted their lives to community service and spiritual reflection. Henry IV had authorised them to construct the monastery in 1603. The building was used as a military hospital in the 1800s and through the two world wars and the Algerian war, then in the 1980s it was an artists' squat for a group who called themselves the Angels of the Récollets; then, only a year ago, it was restored for its current purpose. The original white stone monastery walls have been retained, along with the towers and arcades and windows and sloping roof. To me, it doesn't look like much has changed since the 1600s, and I can feel a lot of old, kind spirits in the walls.

I drift past the acrobats and up to my studio on the second floor. My Studio of Good. It's small, but has tall white windows, a high ceiling with ancient wooden beams, and pylons between them and the cement floor. There's a kitchen, a bathroom, a living area, and a mezzanine for sleeping – a real one, with a floor you can walk around on. The windows reach as high as the mezzanine, which looks out over an expansive park and a children's playground with its steady soundtrack of chatter and squeals. The view is mostly blocked by a giant chestnut tree with lush green leaves, just starting to thin. Birds hop through the boughs and I watch them and feel gloriously alone.

But I do have friends. On the ancient beam above my bed, new characters reveal themselves night after night in the natural gnarls and flecks, old nails and the remnants of paint left by the Angels of the Récollets. The first I noticed, right in the centre, was E.T., the Extra Terrestrial, his triangular skull, and his beady eyes glaring at me. A few nights later I saw the row of baby ducks, then a woman from a hair commercial. Then a shark's head. Then the anatomical diagram of a vagina, with a little knot clit.

I spend the weeks before school begins exploring the neighbourhood – the designer shops and cafés of the Canal Saint-Martin, the markets and brasseries around the Gare de l'Est, the long, solemn boulevard de Magenta. But mostly I find myself back in the rue du Faubourg-Saint-Denis. Nothing makes sense there. Which makes me comfortable because nothing makes sense inside of me either. I spend entire days lost in its different worlds, the spice shops and delicatessens and Asian supermarkets; the fruit market with its shouting men offering tastes of peach and strawberry and cherry; the *parapharmacie* with its pills to suppress your appetite, drain your fat and make your tan last longer. Although vegetarian, I nevertheless marvel at the meats: halal, kosher, tripe, liver, head cheese, lips and ears and tongues, *foie gras frais*. I nibble on sandwiches called *swedishes*, and Pakistani samosas and Russian *pirojkis*, somehow losing my fastidiousness over whether they have any trace of meat products in them.

After surveying the dozen boulangeries around the Récollets, I decide that the one halfway down the rue du Faubourg-Saint-Denis, with its glorious Art Nouveau frontage, has the best bread, and seems to cost the same as anywhere else. The snooty man behind the counter sniffs my blood of an Englishman and does not approve of me one little bit, but I make it immediately clear that I know the game and will not be taking any shit. We develop an unspoken agreement: I will accept him turning his nose up at me (to show the locals his disapproval of an *Anglaise* like me, thus maintaining the social order), in exchange for him giving me the bread I want.

My favourite place on the rue du Faubourg-Saint-Denis is the Festi Bazar, a dilapidated discount store wedged between the fruit market and the Sancak Turkish sandwich shop. I spend hours amongst the piled-up plastic homewares, the wrapping papers and scented candles and powdery incense, the keyrings and necklaces and mirrors and tinsel and toilet brushes. Like the street outside, the Festi Bazar is constantly changing, and there is no rhyme or reason to it. Goods are piled on top of each other, and when something new comes in, it's simply pushed in amongst the rest. If you pull a product out from a shelf a whole stack of things fall. There is so much *stuff* in the Festi Bazar, my brain overloads and I forget almost instantly what I've come in for, and also who and where I am. Which feels nice, and I find myself returning to the bazaar just to stand there and look. The mangy store cat with cancer-bitten ears doesn't mind. Nor does the shopkeeper in her sari. She watches her little TV without looking up, as if I'm not even there. I get the feeling such behaviour is not unusual to her.

At the bottom of the street is a majestic archway, similar to the Arc de Triomphe, with the words *Ludovico Magno* in big gold writing. I read that in the 1300s it was a gateway to Paris, then it was rebuilt as a triumphal arch in the 1600s by Louis XIV to celebrate his military victories. The archway is covered in pigeon shit and rubbish but stands like a proud footnote to all the life going on before it on a daily basis. Its sculpted façade depicts ancient men on horses riding towards people begging not to be killed. Angels blow their trumpets and a lion hangs its head from the top of the arch, tongue out, as though exhausted and thirsty. This is how I feel after too long on the rue du Faubourg-Saint-Denis, when I must return to the Récollets, draw the curtains and sleep for several hours, even in the middle of the day.

The first day of school finally arrives. The blue door is propped open and people gather around it, talking, chaining up bikes, smoking. I follow a group speaking a Scandinavian language down the pathway and through the corridors into the big room with the photos. Bodies in all different colours and shapes and sizes, each wearing the same stretchy black material, move around me, getting closer as the room slowly fills up. To hide my terror I stand for a long time staring at the photo of Jacques Lecoq. *Help me, Jacques.*

There is a clap and everyone sits down. Madame Lecoq gives a welcome speech that I can generally understand and introduces five teachers: a sinewy, grey-haired Frenchman called Claude; a small, cropped-haired Italian woman called Angela; a tall Belgian man called Boris; a short Korean man called Ju-Yong; and a stocky young English guy called Sam. Then she asks us to stand up, one by one, say our names and a sentence about ourselves in French. I make a joke about riding a kangaroo to school, which nobody laughs at, including the three other Australians. Either my joke or my French is bad, likely both.

No time is wasted with get-to-know-you games or trust exercises. We have already been placed into three groups of thirty-five: I am in group A. Each day is split into three classes: *autocours*, movement and acting. Our group starts with *autocours*, the legendary Lecoq practice in which actors create their own theatre according to a weekly theme, to be presented each Friday to the rest of the school. After the uprisings of May '68, the students approached Jacques Lecoq and asked why they didn't make their own theatre rather than just being taught. Jacques thought it was a brilliant idea, and so the *autocours* was born. The first week's theme is 'A Place, an Event'.

Groups B and C move off into other rooms, leaving my group in the foyer. We have to form our own subgroups of seven and, unlike in most theatres, it's a democracy, with no designated director or writer or actors. An awkward shuffling finds me with two Greek girls, a Japanese guy, a Canadian guy, a French girl and an English girl, both called Elodie.

To separate them I call them Élodie France and Elodie England. Then I just call everyone by their country names in my head; it helps me remember them. Elena and Caterina Greece and Elodie England don't speak French. Élodie France doesn't speak English. Yoshi Japan speaks neither French nor English. We spend the entire hour and a half trying to figure out how to communicate. After *autocours* we move into the *Grande Salle* for movement class with Claude, who is wearing a pilled black tracksuit. He tells us he has taught at the school for many years but that he doesn't know anything, so don't ask. Then he sends us running around the room, spreading to each corner, meeting each other and moving away. The pressure of our feet on the sprung wood floors makes a piano somewhere tinkle.

Later, sweating, we move into a smaller room with green vinyl floors; they call this one the *Salle Verte*. Angela, Ju-Yong and Boris are in there. Angela speaks French with her whole mouth, like she is eating Italian food.

'If you don't want to work, and work hard, you should go now,' she says. She talks about listening, and about being present, and then my French hits maximum capacity and I neither retain nor understand a single word more.

Towards the end of the class she asks us to pretend that there's a pool in the room and to mime taking off our clothes, jumping in and swimming from one side to the other. Two French guys and Ravi Canada, who have understood the instructions, get up. An Italian guy called Romeo gets up too, but he hasn't quite grasped it, and to our horror actually starts taking his clothes off, exposing his impressive abs and his dick stuffed in a pair of green Y-fronts. He jumps frantically into the imaginary water. Nobody dares laugh, and Angela, bewildered, says something along the lines of she *wonders what school he thinks he has come to*.

The first week is like drowning. Each of us, with our own languages, with our own levels of French and acting experience, is alone, yet surrounded by bodies, on us, around us, all over us. We each have our stories and our current situations. Some of us are living on floors, one of us sleeps on a pull-out shelf in a kitchen, another has no running water and showers weekly in a gay sauna. One of us is forty-four and has a nine-year-old son and a loft in Belleville with a stocked kitchen and a living room we can rehearse in for *autocours*. Lots of us are called Marc. Some of us are bossy, some too shy to stand up in improvisations, some annoyingly unafraid to jump up before everyone else has had a turn. Some are social, some aren't sure if they're in the right place, some suck up to the teachers, some have excellent flexibility, some are already acrobats, one of us is a famous film star from Spain. Some of us throw parties in the first week, some of us stick to those who speak our own language. But all of us want one thing: to survive the first term, and hopefully the first year. We have come this far.

On Friday afternoon, all the first-years and teachers gather in the *Grande Salle* for the presentation of *autocours*. The students sit on the floor to watch, the teachers on the long bench seat that Claude has started putting across the doors to shin people who rush into class late. The groups get up one by one to perform their scenes. We have decided that our place is to be a café and the event is Yoshi having a heart attack and dying. Before we even get to the heart attack Angela waves her hands above her head and says, 'Okay, *merci!*' We are creamed, as are most of the others, for being too complicated, too small, not creating space, being in our heads. We slink back to sit on the floor, broken, but also broken in.

There's a party afterwards at a bar called Chez Jeannette a few doors down, but I am so exhausted I stagger home and pull the curtains shut before sleeping all night and most of the weekend.

The following weeks are a haze of school, coffee, beer and sleep. The internet is connected in my Studio of Good, which leads to much research and exploration, including my first porn download. The result is thrilling but ultimately lonely, and I fear that the director of the Récollets and the administrators of my grant are watching, so I clear my history and make a pact not to do it again. I will be a Franciscan monk with my grey hoodie on, and engage in spiritual reflection. I do this for five minutes. Then I google my teachers from school: a story comes up from the 1970s about Claude, with a picture of him in a leotard. The film actress from Spain is a serious star, and now I recognise her from some of my favourite films. She is so gentle and understated, you'd never know. The internet death clock says I will die on Saturday 4 April 2048. Not bad considering I clicked 'smoker'. There's an option to delay your date of death, but when I click on it, it just takes me to health sites. In my inbox is an email from Dad with a photo of the family sitting around at a Sunday lunch with too-wide smiles on their faces. An old friend of Mum's is sitting a little too close to Dad. An email from Gabriella saying she's got a new agent and is moving to LA. An email from Jack saying French people smell like cheese and that I should just come home. An email from a friend of a friend, an Australian called Kiki who is also living in Paris. She sounds nice. I write back.

The Hanging of the Cream Bulb

I don't want to go to the party. It's a cold, wet night and Kiki's studio is warm, my belly full of her spinach pie, my head woozy on wine. The muffled wail of a trumpet floats from a dusty radio under piles of paper and crayons and art books. We are seated at her easel as she teaches me to blend oil paints.

'I'll call it *Rain on the Seine*,' I say, wiggling on my stool. 'It could be a masterpiece.'

'Maybe,' says Kiki, standing up and sculling the last of her wine. 'But your lights are dull as dogshit.'

It's true. But if they take me hours to finish we can stay in here all night and drink more wine.

'Come on,' she smiles, and, sensing my game, takes the brushes from my hand and tosses them in turpentine. 'I'll be your best friend.'

She already is, a thousandfold. Since we met a few weeks ago, we've spent almost every spare moment together, mainly here in her studio in the Cité Internationale des Arts, with its ugly lino floors and beautiful view over the Seine and the Île Saint-Louis. She has a residency here from the Art Gallery of New South Wales, and she not only paints, she cooks. There's always something bubbling away in the cluttered kitchenette, with some exotic root vegetable or chickpeas in it. She doesn't even use the tinned ones.

'Shine, shine,' I say, grabbing a cloth and pressing the paint into the canvas. If I can draw it out until nine-thirty maybe she'll give up on dragging me out.

She pulls on some stockings and starts applying eyeliner to her wide Middle Eastern eyes in a mirror on the wall. 'It's perfect now,' she says. 'A masterpiece.'

Kiki must be my complete physical opposite, all curves and dark curls, a goddess from a Fellini film. With her pale skin and deep eyebrows she can wear earrings with beads and jewels, and headscarves, and dark red lipstick that looks like it should be there.

'I'm trying so hard to make it *juste*,' I complain in an exaggerated voice, continuing to blend. This is the it-word at school, and Kiki and I have been having long discussions about it. It's hard to translate: something perhaps between 'true', 'right' and 'faithful'. What is *juste* or *pas juste* can make or break an artwork, whether a painting or a performance, and when I explained the concept to Kiki she had plenty to say about art that was technically great but not *juste*. My *autocours* this week had fallen majorly flat because it was *pas juste*. The subject was 'A Day in the Life of a Square' and we had to observe the movement in a Paris square and then recreate its dynamic as a theatre piece, using the whole *Grande Salle*. My group chose the Place des Abbesses, a quaint, shady square in Montmartre with a merry-go-round in it and wandering, blissed-out tourists, and benches with people kissing and arguing and eating pastries on them. In a small adjoining park is a wall with *I love you* written on it in all different languages. We rehearsed night and day for the entire week but our piece was stopped after only a few minutes and labelled a 'giant soup'. It wasn't enough to recreate the stories from the square, the teachers said, there was no theatre, no dynamic. It wasn't *juste*. I had no idea what any of this meant.

To create something that is *juste*, they told us, we first need to learn how to observe. I go to the window and try to truly look at the lights. There is a lot of white and yellow to them, some blue perhaps, too, amidst the yellow, but that brightness – my brain can't seem to understand how to capture it. I go back to the canvas and dab on more white, blending it with the yellow and grey and some blue, with my fingers. It helps slightly. But mostly the painting looks like a smudged impression of outer space, a pallid shit smear amongst Kiki's exultant abstracts.

'I'll owe you one,' she says. 'Pleeease.'

'Why aren't more children named after paints?' I joke, pretending I haven't heard her as I rummage through a box of paints. 'Carmine and Umber and Madder Lake …'

'Slut.' She fastens her earrings.

I leave the easel and walk around the room, observing her work on the walls exploring dreams and liminal spaces: the deep washes of blues, taupes and reddish-browns studded with the occasional burst of light remind me of the autumnal Paris outside, while also making me feel like I'm looking right inside her. They punch me in the stomach but I can't say why. They are *juste*.

She slings her bag over her shoulder and stands looking at me, eyebrows raised. 'Let's go.'

'Oh dear, I would so love to come,' I sigh, looking down at my clothes spattered with ultramarine and zinc-white and coal-black. 'But look at me. I can't go to a party now.'

'Fuck you!' she laughs, pulling on her boots. 'Goddamn it, I want to stay here too. I want to play gin rummy.'

⁓

The party is at a girl called Martine's, the sister of Kiki's art dealer in Sydney. Martine has bought several of Kiki's paintings. Kiki says showing up is PR. Her bosom jiggles in her top as the métro carriage vibrates and sways and I recount my previous night's dream about a man with a blanked-out face who held a gun in my mouth and pulled the trigger, but the gun didn't go off.

Kiki always wants every detail. 'You didn't feel scared?'

'No,' I say, dislodging a piece of corn chip from my tooth with the corner of my métro ticket. 'Relieved.'

'Interesting that you didn't die.'

'It was a strange feeling. When I woke up I felt grateful to be alive, but in the dream the relief that I was going to die was overwhelming. Like in a horror film when you're so relieved the victim is dead and not being tortured anymore.'

'Do you always dream about death?' Kiki asks.

'Pretty much.'

'Do you dream about your mum?'

My throat tightens. 'No,' I say. 'Never.'

Every night I try. The closest I've got so far is a beach with a dot right down the end, moving towards me. Knowing it was her didn't make me feel any closer to her, or better.

Martine's apartment is in a hidden building behind a giant green door in the boulevard de Magenta, not far from the Récollets, which is convenient for when I need to bust out. I am still in a monk-like state of mind. Apart from drinks after school, this is the most social I've been since I arrived.

Her doorway is open and we walk straight in, past one of Kiki's most majestic paintings. There are creaky floorboards and lovely tall windows, and high white ceilings with frosted curls and angels in the corners. It's achingly beautiful, and Martine is too, the bowl of her pelvis jutting from her slinky black dress as she sweeps in to kiss us both.

'So glad you could come,' she exhales.

The party is throbbing with bourgeois bohemians. Kiki has been educating me on all the Paris types. Bourgeois bohemians, or bobos, are the well-to-do young creative professionals who live on the Right Bank, buy organic food and dress relaxed-chic. For parties, Kiki points out, they usually wear one fancy item, such as a sequinned skirt, matched with a down-to-earth item, perhaps a rough-looking T-shirt or a pair of trainers, or something weird, like a necklace made of a cassette tape. It's about contrast. No eye makeup, but hot-pink lipstick. High snakeskin heels with casual print pants. The hair has an I-don't-care perfection.

Kiki is more bohemian than bourgeois, with her beaded jewellery, embroidered skirt and army boots. Martine looks more bourgeois than bohemian in her dazzling top-to-toe outfit with no contrasting item, her perfect makeup and hair. I look like an unemployed construction worker in my paint-flecked jumper and jeans, frizzy post-rain hair tucked up into one of Jack's old man hats.

It's a house-warming, a *pendaison de crémaillère*. This literally means 'the hanging of the cream bulb'. In the old days the guests would bring cream. We've brought a cheap bordeaux. There's an Australian theme: a flag with a boxing kangaroo is draped across the walls, and INXS blares from a mixing desk manned by a model wearing bunny ears. French murmurs are occasionally pierced by the twang of an English vowel. It starts to rain heavily outside, dulling all the sounds to a watery murmur.

Kiki and I pour glasses of wine from someone else's bottle and find a place to sit next to a plate of cheese on toothpicks and sausages in bread – an homage to Australian cuisine. I'm not sure why, but for the first time in over a decade, the sausage suddenly smells good. Kiki grabs one and stuffs it into her glorious mouth. I find myself reaching in slow motion for my own.

'Do it,' she says, eyes fierce.

I am tired of my old self. My boring Australian self. I want to belong. I want yang. I hold the sausage up to my face and bite off a rubbery end. As my mouth becomes awash with an ungodly saltiness my gaze drifts towards the doorway.

A guy is standing there. The cardboard cut-out of Frenchman. Tall, dark, rain-slick, a vision in a long black coat. His cigarette is still lit despite the elements: the cliché is that strong. Did the sausage conjure him? I can't be certain he is real. He peels off his coat, cigarette defying all laws of matter as it's pulled through the sleeve and back to his lips, still alight, before being stubbed out in Martine's fancy gold ashtray. She and a flock of females descend on him, and the blond-haired guy he's come with, and they disappear.

Kiki nudges me. 'Good girl!'

I take another bite and smile at her.

She continues chewing, eyes wide, watching my mouth before turning to watch the blond wingman, who has just slid back into the room in his socks, brandishing a magnum of champagne.

'*C'est la TEUF!*' he shouts. *Teuf*, I tell Kiki, means 'fête' – in *verlan*. Party. I have been learning this type of street slang from Étienne at school, who I initially couldn't understand a word of in *autocours*. *Verlan* stands for *l'envers* – the reverse – and there's a whole language made out of it, originally as drug- and sex-trade code. My favourite expression is '*C'est un truc de ouf quoi.*' This stands for *truc de fou*, which means 'crazy thing', and you say this sentence when something is amazing. The sentence has a fantastic guttural sound to it, and I've been using it as much as I can, driving my schoolmates and Kiki crazy.

The blond guy approaches and Kiki instinctively holds out her glass. The dark guy follows him as they walk around introducing themselves.

'Raphaël,' says the blonde, reaching down to kiss me on both cheeks before filling my glass. I know I should stand but I miss the moment, and besides, is he seriously going to kiss every person at this party? There must be sixty of us.

'Jayne,' I say politely, moving my face left and right of his. '*Enchanté.*'

Raphaël has a high forehead, dainty lips, and is wearing a pink-and-white striped shirt tucked into high-waisted jeans. I try to imagine an Australian guy wearing pink. He moves on to Kiki, who stands and does the proper kiss ritual. The dark guy approaches me and I stand up this time. He turns his head to one side and places his cheek gently to mine, right then left. Our cheeks don't quite touch but the little hairs on the skin reach out to each other: a thousand pins of electricity.

'Adrien.'

'Jayne.' I don't say 'enchanted' but I am, deeply. His eyes are almost black and his jaw is wide, with lots of teeth in it. His brows have seen some ancient wars. A piece of hair falls in his eyes and he flicks it back with a sniff, as though he is going to say something, but he doesn't. When he steps towards Kiki he leaves behind a musky scent.

I sit down and neck my champagne, wishing I'd at least had a shower. Kiki gives me a look. 'Aristos,' she says. 'Classic ones from the posh parts of Paris. Rarely seen around these parts.'

'Not bobos?'

'Definitely not bobos.'

Later, as I'm talking to the DJ bunny, Kiki manoeuvres the dark Frenchman towards me.

'Jayne, did you meet Adrien? He's an actor too.'

'Oh?' I say, never sure what this means. Kiki leaves with the bunny, and Adrien and I stand in silence for a moment.

'My Eengleesh very shit,' he says, so we speak in French, despite my not feeling confident at all. I ask him what sort of acting he does, though I hate being asked that question myself – it's a stupid question. What are you supposed to say? ANYTHING I CAN GET, WHY, DO YOU KNOW OF SOMEONE LOOKING FOR SOMEONE TO DO SOMETHING?! He tells me he's doing a film course with an American director in Saint-Germain. A method thing.

'*Et toi?*'

I tell him about the theatre school and he hasn't heard of it, but that doesn't matter. I can't take my eyes off the gap between his two front teeth when he smiles. He says he likes my hat. We talk about the cold outside and how winter seems to have come early, in October. I act as if I know that's unusual. He asks about the paint on my jumper and I tell him about Kiki and lead him out into the entranceway to show him her painting. It's an early work of a tree in a bleary, ice-green landscape. The figure is limp inside the thick distortion of colour, white melding with muted blue and hints of yellow. It's as though we're looking at it through a dirty lens or a fogged window or the blurred vision of age. He says it gives him *chair de poule*. I don't know what that is, so he shows me – goosebumps, all the way up his forearms. I have them too, not just on my arms, but my neck and back and other places, and I'm not sure if it's him or the painting or the combination of both. I love that he can see the terror of Kiki's work, even in the simplicity of a tree.

He pours me more champagne and lights my cigarette with a match from a little matchbox that has a picture of a skier on it and the words *Style. Fun. Gliss.* We laugh at the dumbness of the words. I do some funny skiing actions to show what I think the word *gliss* might mean and he laughs again. He says he likes Sweden. I tell him I'm from Australia.

He wants to hug a koala, he says. I tell him they scratch. He raises one lovely eyebrow and leans against the wall, exhaling a plume of smoke above my head, cigarette at first knuckle. We stand talking for longer than I think and make our voices louder as the music gets louder, and I want to ask for his number but can't seem to find the right place in the conversation.

It's suddenly late and Kiki wants to leave. Adrien and I say goodbye and again there's the tiny cheek antennae as I wind my scarf tight around my neck. He waves from the doorway as Kiki and I stumble down the stairs and out into the inky night. The rain has stopped and a cloud of mist hangs in the lamplight.

Kiki huddles my arm under her jacket as we walk towards the métro. 'Not going home with Paco Rabanne then,' she says.

'No,' I say. 'But now I know how to paint a Frenchman.'

'Did you get his number?'

'No.'

'What?' She stops. 'Why?'

'*Wat?* Hawaii?' mocks a passing motorcyclist in a thick French accent.

'I don't know,' I moan. 'Surely he has a girlfriend.'

'He doesn't! I asked him.'

We walk a few more steps before she stops sharply. 'Ooh!' she says, feeling around herself. 'I forgot my umbrella.' And she turns on her heels and leaves me stranded in the mist, returning moments later with a Cheshire grin and a number scrawled on the back of an old métro ticket.

'*Voilà,*' she says. 'Ring-a-root.'

The phone wakes me the next morning.

'Did the sausage digest?' says Kiki.

I curl up, still half in a dream. 'Don't know yet.'

'Did you ring the Frenchman?'

'No. I had weird dreams. An orange beach, a desert. Mum's butterscotch pudding. I was in it, I couldn't breathe.'

'Can you write it?'

'Don't think so.'

'Well, get your crayons out and draw it, call that Frenchman, then meet me at the Montreuil markets. I want to go and buy a whole lot of junk I don't need.'

I lie in bed wondering if I really want to ring Adrien. I don't want to get into a relationship. No *relationship*, says Kiki in my head. Good Time Fun Experimentation. She's right. What harm can it do?

I eat two mini toasts from a box, which tear at the roof of my mouth, and try to draw the butterscotch-pudding tower asphyxiation, but I can't, so I write some words with diagrams and arrows. Then I pull the métro ticket from my jacket pocket. You're just going to run off with some Frenchman, says Jack in my head. We were at the beach the day before I left. He said he would come with me if I wanted him to, be my maid, eat pastries. I laughed. Though Jack made the world feel warm, I didn't want him to come. And though there was no Frenchman whatsoever in my mind, something rang true in what Jack said. I was going to run off into the darkness and never look back.

Drawing breath, I dial the number. Message bank. His voice is chocolate. I leave a confused message in terrible Franglais, suggesting we meet up to further discuss 'methods', and hang up, feeling like an idiot. But it does feel good to engage in some seduction.

⁓

'*Deux euros*,' says Kiki to the shoe-seller, defiant. Her French is an abomination but that never holds her back.

'*Trois cinquante*,' he says, nudging his skullcap and meeting her glare.

'*Deux euros*,' she insists, mutilating both vowel sounds with her thick Australian accent.

'*Deux cinquante*.'

'*Deux*.'

They face off, silent. The seller's wife comes to his side, nursing a knotty-haired baby. The man breaks into a smile and Kiki wins again, this time a pair of vintage silver pumps. She claps and puts them in her hessian bag, along with the array of scarves, beads and an old, rusted candelabra.

'Montreuil shits on the big *puces*,' she says as we walk off to find the crêpe stand.

These flea markets are another world from the famous ones I've visited at the Porte de Saint-Ouen. There, the stalls are ordered and neat, and things are expensive. Here, it's cheap, and mayhem; swarms of people buzz around stalls piled with colourful clothes and junk, the smell of mothballs and waffles and foot odour and roasted chestnuts making me dizzy. A man sits singing on a pile of old bicycles. A gypsy guitarist and a pipe band and two piano-accordionists battle it out for the prime spot. It's mad and fun but freezing, the blinding sun and clear blue sky belying a cold I can hardly believe. My teeth chatter, even though I'm wearing all the clothes I own on top of each other.

Kiki hands me a steaming chocolate crêpe and a paper cup of coffee.

'We need to find you some real winter clothes,' she says, sizing me up. 'You'll perish.'

'It's okay,' I say. 'It can't get colder than this, surely.'

'Are you kidding? It's autumn!'

I hug myself tighter. A man begins playing his accordion in front of us. We drop a few coins into his little leather pouch and move away.

'Has he called back yet?' she asks.

I check my phone. 'No.'

'Intriguing!' She rubs her mittens together. 'What else shall we look at?'

'All kinds of junk we don't need?'

'Yes!' she laughs. 'How much money have you got?'

'Twenty euros.'

'Fucking plenty!'

After hours of rummaging, sneezing and haggling we catch the métro home together, planning a trip to a department store to buy a *doudoune* – one of the marshmallow coats that have instantly turned the fashionable women of Paris into a parade of waddling Michelin women.

I found nothing in the way of a warm coat at the markets, and Mum's leather trench is simply not doing the job.

'*Merci madame*,' says an African woman in a colourful headdress with a baby strapped to her back as Kiki offers up her seat in the métro.

'Do you get called *madame*?' I ask as we stand clinging to the pole, bags around us. Kiki is four years older than me: is that what makes the difference?

'Always.'

'Why? I'm *mademoiselle*.'

'I don't know. The boobs? If I wear a dress and plait my hair I sometimes get *mademoiselle*.'

'I thought *madame* was just when you're married.'

'But how can they tell?'

'Yeah, I guess. So they think you look married but not me?'

'They think I look old.'

I did get *madame*'d once. It was when I had my hair up and was going to the bank to try to open an account. Though I had a letter from the government office that manages my scholarship, I kept getting shunted from one branch to the next. After several frustrating days I decided to try an experiment. I went home, changed out of my janky theatre blacks and into the most presentable clothes I owned, applied makeup and put my hair in a neat bun. Back at the bank, the woman at the front desk called me *madame* and the manager, though he tried to deny me once more, found me more difficult to argue with. Also, I cried. This, like the Lesson of the Burnt Baguette, I filed away for future reference. Performance is everything. Including costume. In Paris you need to look the part for the audience to which you are playing, otherwise life is more difficult. I will never wear track pants to a bank meeting again. I'll be as *madame* as I can.

We pull into the Gare de l'Est and Kiki and I kiss goodbye. 'Tell me if he calls,' she says, before the train disappears down the tunnel.

I have way too much stuff. It takes me ten minutes to struggle my way up the steps with my ridiculous purchases, which include a torn, red

velvet Louis XIV chair, several random lengths of pretty fabric, a lovely
long white curtain with flowers embroidered on it, two tea towels, and a
green dress with no zip. Four bags of junk, with a few useful pieces, such
as a pilled red cashmere scarf and a furry hat with earflaps. It feels odd
to have bought a hat with flaps that have been over someone else's ears,
but it didn't smell too bad and Kiki said I would be grateful when the
time came.

Having climbed my way out of the station I set my chair on the
ground and collapse on it to catch my breath. I take in the view of the
old hotels and grand old brasseries with their faded frontages and signs
advertising daily *formules* and specialties from France's eastern region,
sauerkraut and sausage and crisp white wines. The streets are full of the
usual hustle of cars and bikes and buses that fart black smoke. Dizzy
tourists flap maps like pigeons' wings, and the pigeons themselves flap
amongst the dirt and scum beneath the bins and across the squares.
Streetsweepers in fluoro-green stand sipping coffee in a *tabac* across the
road, the floor covered in ash and lotto tickets and peanut shells. Men
with smooth brown faces and pale green eyes gather around telephone
boxes smeared in graffiti. A waiter in his black and white costume grunts
and spits a bubbled glob in the gutter. Bobos clutching baskets full of
bread and cheese and wine make their way to the banks of the Canal
Saint-Martin. The bells at the fume-stained Église Saint-Laurent in its
piss-soaked cement triangle start gonging.

As two gypsy girls approach me, I crush my cigarette with the point
of my boot, collect my bags and shuffle towards the Récollets. When
I first arrived I fell prey to their 'Do you speak English?' routine,
and discovered a small hand in my rear pocket before the girls ran
giggling away.

There's no room in my place for any more clutter but I'm pleased with
my purchases. The green dress will be a project, and perhaps I can make
something with all the pretty fabric. The velvet chair sits in the middle
of the room, proud, alone, utterly out of place. The fabric underneath
the seat is torn and there's a stain on its lovely red cushion, which I tell
myself is an innocent splash of wine. The white curtain is superfluous,

as the window is too high and already has a perfectly measured, long red blackout curtain on it. I will put it in my new apartment one day, I decide, the real, grown-up one with the curled ironwork and window boxes.

I open the window and light a cigarette, letting the freezing night air hit my face. A knock at the door: it's Miru, the little boy from down the hall. He is five and has a Japanese artist dad and an Austrian film-maker mother and thus speaks four languages: French at school, Japanese with him, German with her, and English with both of them. And with me. We play dress-ups for a while – he likes my new hat, though it messes up his self-styled spike hairdo; the green dress falls neatly over his compact Japanese frame, and he puts on my highest heels to try to get it higher off the ground, sashaying back and forth. His mother, Tatiana, peeks in the open doorway. 'Miru! It's dinner time. Stop bothering Jayne.'

'He's not at all,' I say.

Miru gives me a kiss and runs out. I crawl upstairs to the mezzanine with my phone. No messages.

Fire

I am a bushfire. Electricity shoots from the tips of my toes to the top of my head. Fits of sizzling. I tear at the air, turning all in my path to dust. My arms flail; I convulse, burn, sting, attack, spin and spit, until finally, exhausted, my fire, having destroyed a small village, hisses at the rain before dulling to a pale ember and disappearing.

'*Pas mal*,' says Claude's voice from above me as I lie puffing and wheezing on the floor with four of my classmates, also in pools of themselves in front of the silent class. '*Un bel espace de feu.*'

A beautiful space of fire? My face begins to burn on the green linoleum. I haven't had anything close to a *pas mal* yet.

Claude starts telling the class things he liked about my fire, which I can barely understand – he talks like a hurricane. When he finishes I pull myself up, trying to hide my red cheeks. But my classmates' eyes aren't on me. It wasn't my *pas mal*. Like Claude, they're all staring at Marie-France.

Marie-fucking-France. Perfect, Parisian Marie-France, with her milky skin and straight brown hair. Marie-France has already had several *pas mals* and even a few *biens*. She's not far off a *très bien*, I imagine, even perhaps an *excellent*. Marie-France – what kind of a name is that, when you're from France? Umi Japan, Meg London, Faye Ohio.

Marie-France *France*. In the primordial ooze of the first months of school, she has managed to convey some sort of grace. She does *juste* without trying.

She stands there receiving her compliment from Claude. I notice that her two longest toes on each foot are webbed, which makes me feel slightly better. Claude moves on to talk about Laurent Marseille's fire, which, he says, had no soul. Laurent is defensive and asks questions, and I realise that we non-French-speakers are actually at an advantage: we can't fight back, so we have no choice but to listen and evolve. The room is tense as Laurent's veins pulsate in his neck. Claude huffs and says something cutting that makes him shut up and sit down. Claude turns to me. '*Et toi, Jenny.*'

I've stopped trying to correct him. I sit forward and strain my entire body to listen. 'Too *said*. Telephone? Self-something.' I'm disappointed; I truly thought I had found something in fire. Air, water, earth – these elements had each fascinated me during our explorations of their physicality, but fire was something else. I really thought it was my element.

Angela stands and turns to the class, her powerful arms reaching out in their expressive Italian way. 'There was *something* inside Jayne's fire.' I perk up. 'But why didn't it work?'

Shrugs all around. One classmate offers that I was too inside it. Shut up, Sweden, I think to myself, your fire was an epileptic dog.

'You need to work on your feet,' she says, pointing at my raw, blistered toes. 'They make us want to laugh, even though you are very serious.'

'What *is* fire?' says Claude to the class. 'Have you really watched it?'

I have – I've lit matches, imagined it, dreamt it, googled it. Perhaps I was trying to paint what I had seen, rather than be inside it. That's all I can gather from what they're saying. And that I have weird feet.

Claude claps his hands. 'Okay. Next.'

Another group jumps up. Their fire is all manner of mush, with the odd flickering ember. Angela sits watching with intense seriousness, chin in hands. Claude sits in his usual position, long, sinewy legs crossed over each other. He smiles, shakes his head, and puts his face in his hands. God knows how many fires he has sat through in his years teaching here.

I wish I'd seen Marie-France's fire. The physical engagement required to muster even a flicker is staggering – you have to abandon yourself completely, and yet not so completely that you go to the other side, which Steve Dublin is currently doing, making me giggle into my leg warmers. He is so *in* the fire he's actually in a spasmic sort of trance. Meg London is occasionally getting it – her engagement is controlled yet wild. Marc Finland does some convincing sparks but is too good-looking to truly summon fire.

The class is exhausting, and at the end of the day we decamp to Chez Jeannette. It's been tradition since the school began, for students to come here, with its cracked tile floors and wedding-cake ceilings and cancan-girl wallpaper and beautiful bar lit with squiggly lights reading *Chez Jeannette*. The scratched mirrors all the way along the back wall reflect the dim light of red chandeliers and long red leather banquettes and old formica tables that, pushed together, can entertain an entire class of rowdy theatre school students.

We post-mortem the day's efforts with beers and kirs at the bar, smoking and ashing on the floor. There are no ashtrays on the bar, to eliminate the possibility of ashing in someone's drink. It's illegal *not* to ash on the floor, but I still keep expecting Mum to tap on my shoulder and haul me out, saying with clenched teeth, 'And while I'm at it *don't* smoke.' On Étienne's Marlboro Light packet are the French words for *SMOKING LEADS TO A LONG AND PAINFUL DEATH*. I take a drag on mine and think how sometimes you can die a long and painful death from lung cancer even if you don't smoke. So you might as well.

Étienne is from the Paris suburbs and, chuffed by my intrigue at the rhythmic way he speaks, is teaching me a steady stream of new expressions. When I say this cigarette is *truc de ouf quoi* he rolls his eyes and laughs. His name sounds like a girl's, though he assures me it's a boy's, as is Camille, the name of a guy in Group C. Étienne says a girl can't be called Étienne. The Spanish girl who looks like the girl from the film *Amélie* comes and bums a cigarette off Étienne. She tells me my fire was good, just that it didn't really work. The Spanish Amélie can say things like that to me because she's so cute. I make a mental note to work with her on the next *autocours*.

My stomach growls so I excuse myself and squeeze through the crowd and go next door to buy a hot three-cheese panini from the Lebanese bakery. I take it back to the bar but Jeannette gives me a foul look, so I give the others a consolatory wave and walk up the rue du Faubourg-Saint-Denis, huddled over it, eating.

'*Bon appétit,*' says a woman in a furry jacket standing with her arms folded outside her shop.

'*Merci,*' I smile.

'*Bon appétit,*' call two workmen in unison, leaning against the post office wall.

'*Merci.*'

'*Bon appétit,*' says the man outside the kebab stand opposite the Gare de l'Est.

Oh. I get it. You don't eat while you walk. I go back to the Récollets, close my door and stuff the rest down in front of my almost naked tree.

Still no messages.

La Patache

Almost two weeks after I left the message for Adrien, my phone rings. I'm down in the park, playing in the nearly frozen sandpit with Miru.

'*Allô Jayne?*'

'*Oui?*'

'*C'est Adrien.*'

My heart starts to pound. I'd almost given up on him. '*Oh! Salut Adrien.*'

Miru kicks cold sand in my eye. I grab him, trying to avoid the snot rivers down his front. Phone calls in French are hard, and I try to be cool but my words are spinning out of control and I keep saying *oui* over and over. I can make out that he has been somewhere, or something happened, and he wasn't able to call me sooner.

'*Ce n'est pas grave,*' (it doesn't matter) I say, grateful for that phrase at least.

'Are you free tonight to take the *apéro*?' he asks politely in English, perhaps sensing my hysteria.

We arrange to meet at my favourite bar on the Canal Saint-Martin and I say, 'See you there! *J'attends avec impatience!*' The desperation of it: I'm waiting impatiently. Why can't I figure out how to say a simple 'looking forward to it'?

Miru and I build a sand sculpture shaped like a fish – he likes sea creatures – then I take him back up to his room. Tatiana opens the door with a smile and thrusts me a twenty, which I hand back, but she jams it into my pocket and goes inside calling, 'You have to take it!'

Miru wraps his little arms around me and says, 'Wait! Jun! I have *cadeau* for you.' He runs inside and comes back out with a picture he did with crayons and watercolours at school. It's a serpent girl with yellow dots all over her head, in a sea with a giant sun rising over it. She has very long eyelashes and a triangular dress and enormous boobs, though I'm an A-cup. In the sky is written *Miru LOVE JUN*.

I hug him tight and kiss his soft little cheek. He farts deeply in my arms and maybe follows through, so I nudge him in through the doorway and pull it shut.

Twenty minutes to sculpt myself into someone – who? The mirror reveals a hopeful face, young but old, lines in thinking places on my forehead. A pimple on its way out. A bit of basil in my front teeth. My blond hair has gone darker and I feel like dying it white, or perhaps bright red. Nobody in Paris seems to do crazy hair like that. There aren't even very many blondes. My skin is less pale since I started eating meat. Cheeks flushed with excitement, the cold, the new iron levels in my blood. I pull my hair back off my face, smear on some foundation and then rub most of it off. A hint of pink lipstick. A touch of grey on the eyes. Special Dress? No, too special. Black dress, stockings, boots, a black cap – not the Russian flap hat. Mum's trusty leather coat.

Chantal, the *directrice* of the Récollets, intercepts me on the way out with a parcel from home. I rush back upstairs and rip it open: a selection of Australian sweets and a postcard of a taxidermy koala with my sister's writing on the back. *Stuff you. Come home.* I put a few Sherbies and Clinkers in my pocket and slam the door shut.

It's freezing as I run out into the glaring winter sunset. The sky is so bright I have to shield my eyes along the Quai de Valmy. When I reach the bar it's empty but for Adrien, who is sitting up the back, leaning against a wall with torn rose wallpaper on it. A single ray of sunlight slices him in two and he smiles when he sees me, pushing his hair back off his face. I move towards him and bend down, putting my face either side of his.

'Hello,' he says.

'*Bonjour*,' I say.

I sit and take off a few of my layers.

'I like this place,' he says once I'm finally settled in. '*C'est cosy.*'

La Patache is a run-down old bar full of rickety wooden tables and wooden bench seats with no cushions and bottles on shelves with prices written on them in chalk. Your butt gets sore after about an hour, which is why it's perfect for *apéro*. It's run by Monsieur Vito, a lovely old drunk with a big red nose who in my head I call Monsieur Vino. On a graffitied wall in the toilet are French words that translate as something like: *If wine preserves, M. Vito will live to 1000. Long live Patache!* Monsieur Vito has not been in the bar for several weeks, and I'm concerned the alcohol isn't doing its job.

Monsieur Vito's son, Carlo, comes over and kisses me on both cheeks, which makes me feel like a local, and Adrien and I order two Affligem beers. The little oven is stoked and Carlo puts chestnuts on top of it to roast. My cheeks start to thaw out.

Adrien says he's never been to La Patache before but knows the area a bit. I discovered the bar when I met with Faye Ohio, who lives a few doors down, to discuss our *autocours*. I come here a lot, even on my own.

Adrien digs his hands into his cream jumper; he is more casually dressed this time and looks relaxed, though I can tell he is shy. He pulls out a packet of cigarettes and we smoke and sip the beer from fishbowl glasses, flipping between English and French.

'What's a *patache*?' I ask. I picture it as some kind of potato.

He says he's not quite sure but that it's definitely not a potato – maybe a type of small ship. That makes sense, as the bar has a ship-cabin feel, in a storm. We order a plate of sliced meats, my first, and he shows me how to peel the skin off the edge of the dry sausage, though he eats the skin on his. He has large, thick hands, which he makes fun of, calling them *mains de boucher*, which I translate as butcher's hands, and he reassures me that my French is fine. He tells me the canal was once used to bring food into the centre of the city; now it just ferries tourists through its murky waters in slow motion. I have watched these tourists and felt uncomfortable for them as they sat there waving, unable to run. I would hate to be on display like that. So would Adrien, I discover. Though we both like being on stage. That's different, he says, we have the choice.

Adrien has never wanted to run off stage, nor has he had moments, as I have, where he's wanted to pull his pants down. He laughs when I say this, and a little bit of sausage comes out of his mouth but I pretend not to notice. He tells me he has just auditioned for a play and is waiting for the response. And that tonight he has his film-acting class so he can't stay too long. The course is in English, he says, so he can perhaps go to America to work in film. We are talking more in English now; he seems to be making an effort to do this, perhaps because he's on my terms, in my favourite bar.

A Sherbie falls out of my pocket and Adrien asks what it is. I give it to him and he unwraps and eats it, eyes bulging in disbelief as the sugary foam fills his mouth. I tell him about other Australian sweets and my dad's need to supply me with a steady stream of them, as if to remind me of all I'm missing back home. We keep drinking beer and Adrien smiles as I try to make him say Caramello Koala. He helps me say foie gras. I discover he's younger than me and that's a surprise, but it doesn't matter and now things are blurred and my hand is quite close to his but I don't dare touch him. We talk about winter and Kiki and language and travel and Jeunet-Caro films and the amazingness of the internet and I start to wonder how many steps there are between here and my studio, but then he has to leave. I insist on paying the bill. We share the last beer and I'm regretful it's the last and I walk him to the métro at République, where he kisses me on both cheeks though I'm hoping he'll go for the lips. But both kisses touch the skin. The hairs on my neck stand on end, as do my nipples deep in their winter layers. He says next time he will invite me to his favourite place, smiles, and disappears down the staircase.

A small fire glows in my belly as I wander home via the boulevard de Magenta, making the air feel even colder. I tug my scarf up around my ears as I pass a man pissing in full view over a pile of plastic bags, and wonder how his dick doesn't snap off. In my distraction I step in spew – or is it curry – whatever it is, it's slippery and I vow to never take my eyes off where I'm walking again, especially in the boulevard de Magenta.

Window-licking

Kiki tells me to meet her in the section of the Galeries Lafayette with the plastic legs shooting up everywhere. When I arrive she's in a corner with her hand wedged up inside a red-patterned stocking.

'Bit slutty,' I say, tugging at the lycra.

'Perfect!'

As the saleslady wraps up the stockings, we laugh at the word 'gusset', and Kiki pulls up her skirt and flashes me hers. I fall to my knees laughing like I've been kicked in the stomach, banging my head on the counter, which makes us laugh even more, though my head really hurts. The saleslady gives us a look of perfect disdain.

'Did you know the French call window-shopping "window-licking"?' I say as we make our way to the escalator, past the socks and sneezy perfume counters.

But Kiki is only interested in hearing about the date at La Patache.

'I thought it would just be a cool sex fling,' she says after I've recounted the details.

'Me too!'

'Now,' she says, leading me towards the coat section. 'To the doodoonas.'

'Oh, must we?'

Doodoona is Kiki's word for the dreaded *doudoune*. It's like wearing a down quilt tied around your body, with equal sex appeal. They seem to me constrictive, numbing – I can't imagine life with such a thick layer between myself and air. Kiki, having experienced many European winters, swears by hers. It is worn into her body now, so isn't as boxy as many, but it does turn her into a deep-purple cheese puff.

'We must,' says Kiki, grabbing me by the elbow. She pulls a blue, ankle-length coat from a rack and holds it against me. 'How about this little number?'

'Lovely,' I say, peeling it away and moving towards a striped top, gasping at the price tag. Kiki continues rifling through the rack of padded misery as I drift from ugly practicals to sexy unneccessaries.

'I went to Disneyland with my dream guy last night,' she says, examining a black monstrosity. Norbert is from Kiki's dream class, not to be confused with the man of her dreams. He is a nice, corporate German man. Kiki has been examining what it's like to be with someone she is not attracted to. Her data is complete, she tells me: good once. You feel yourself in a whole new light. Not twice.

'He gave me two magnums of fancy champagne.'

'Did you go on the teacups?'

'It wasn't in the fun park, it was in a conference centre.'

'A conference centre in Disneyland?'

'It's a shame, his dreams were really out there.'

'I can't believe there's a conference centre at a fun park.'

'So, no more Norbert.' She pauses a moment. 'And more Zahir.'

'Who's Zahir?'

Zahir is a Palestinian dancer who recently moved in to the Cité with his theatre troupe. He came to her studio the other night with friends and stayed last, drooling into her mouth while he was on top of her, which, she says, wasn't disgusting.

'Ew!' I say, fondling a black silk dress.

'If Norbert had done that …'

'Nobody has ever drooled in my mouth, I don't think,' I say. 'But I did have someone come in my eye once. It swelled up like I'd been punched.

And I know a guy who accidentally came in his own mouth, as he jacked off on the couch. He was mortified.'

Kiki does that laugh where she stops breathing and goes silent, which makes me laugh so hard I go silent too, tears dripping down my face.

'Zahir's got an incredible dick,' she says after she's pulled herself back together, taking a pair of thick winter pants off the rack and holding them up against herself. 'It's long and lithe, just like his dancer's body. Dicks don't always reflect the bodies they're on, do they? But his looks just like him.'

I think for a moment about the dicks I've seen. 'It's not always easy to assess. You don't get much of a chance to look at them. And they have their different moods.'

'I look at them a lot.'

'I wonder if our boobs and lady parts look like us.'

'Probably not.'

'Look at this,' I say, holding up the dress and moving it back and forth through the air, marvelling at the way it ripples and flows like water.

'That won't stop your tits turning into coins and sliding off,' she says, but I'm already heading to the change rooms.

It's one of those terrifying ones with a communal mirror outside, which means you have to come out and parade yourself. As I stand in Dad's pilled explorer socks, looking at my pasty reflection in front of a growing queue of impatient Parisiennes, a man with a nametag on his lapel saying *Gaspard* buzzes around me squealing, *'Non non non, c'est moche!'*

The Parisiennes nod and murmur. Yes, yes, ugly ugly. Gaspard pulls and prods and swats and tuts and *oh la la, non non non*s with a look on his face like he just smelt off foie gras. But he is right, the dress is ugly on me. The front panels and straps are meant for a woman with boulders, not bee stings. Where it should fan Monroe-like, it just flops and sighs.

'Merci,' I whimper, and withdraw behind the velvet curtain. Though my cheeks are sizzling, I do appreciate his honesty. In Australia the salesgirl would have said it looked *amazing* and I would have brought

it home, to do nothing but admire its coathanger majesty. I respect that, for Gaspard, the life of the dress is more important than his desire to make his quota.

I slink back out, past the waiting ladies who have seen too much of me. Kiki is staring blank-faced at a fox-fur coat.

'No go?' she says.

'No, ugly ugly.' I lead her towards the escalators.

'But – the doodoona!' she protests, turning back.

'Beauty is pain,' I insist, and it truly is as we walk out into the icy wind. We ride the métro back to Pont Marie, talking about dicks and vaginas and beauty and practicality. Kiki suggests we go to her favourite little bistro on the riverbank near her place, and it's so warm in there I take off three layers, to Kiki's one. We order split-pea soup and afterwards a warm chocolate fondant with a dollop of cream on top.

'I am really hungry all the time,' I say after gulping down the pudding in about three mouthfuls and wondering if it would be acceptable to order another.

'Well, it's getting seriously cold outside, so your body, sensing no doodoona, is adding its own layer of seal blubber.'

'Oh, well. I can't imagine Coco Chanel in a doodoona.'

Kiki smiles over her teacup.

'No,' I declare, 'my mind is made up. I will weather this Paris winter in style.'

'You'll die –'

'AND', I interrupt, 'Like the seal, come up clapping.'

Kiki laughs. 'Fair enough. I'll make lots of cake.'

We kiss goodbye on the freezing riverbank and I meander back through the Marais, buying a little pink glass bowl from a neon-lit shop called C'EST QUOI to drink coffee out of in the mornings, like the Florents used to do. I can't afford the bowl – my small monthly stipend from the scholarship has to last another week – but it feels good to forget that for a moment. An icy breeze whips through me and I pull Mum's coat tighter around me as I descend into the deserted métro cavern, grateful for its warm, stinky air.

It's too silent back in my room so I put on Cat Power loud while I pick at the ingrown hairs on my legs with a safety pin until they bleed. There's some vodka left in the bottle on the windowsill so I drink the last of it with apple juice, like Kiki does. Then I eat a Caramello Koala, brush my teeth and climb up to the mezzanine, sending a message to Adrien on a whim: *Hi Adrien, hope to see you soon, yesterday was tres agreeable.*

He writes back ten minutes later with the proper accents on his letters: *Très agréable for me too. I call you soon. Je t'embrasse.*

Je t'embrasse means 'I kiss you' and the thought of actually connecting with his lips gives me a little buzz. I think of the skin on his cheeks and his big butcher hands, the veins on the surface as he peeled a sausage. I wonder what his body is like beneath all those winter clothes. My own body stirs; my usual set of characters and scenes make way for Adrien's hands, but he doesn't hang around long – an Anaïs Nin scene I read recently in the back of a bookshop takes over and delivers me to the place I desire to go, then I drift off to sleep, hand in crotch, to dream of caravans in distant landscapes and the gypsy girls from the Gare de l'Est surrounding me, suffocating.

Kiss by the Hôtel de Ville

Days go by before Adrien calls and leaves a polite message saying hello, he hopes I'm well, and perhaps we could see each other soon. I sit on a stoop outside school to listen to his message, frustrated at the length of time between calls while enjoying what it is doing to my adrenaline levels. I listen to his message three more times, then, instead of calling straight back, stand and make my way up the street.

Outside the Bollywood video shop a decrepit, alcohol-bloated man asks for coins but I say no. When I started school I gave money to every soul who asked on my way from the Récollets. Then, in danger of being late for school, I started prioritising, giving only to those with a physical ailment, or those with children. Now I play a lottery based on nothing but the moment. I am horrified at how hard I've become, and the drunk man's defeated 'Fuck I'm hungry' behind my back makes me ill at myself. I run and break my twenty in the boulangerie but he's long gone. The sadness over the man and the delight of Adrien's message coagulate in my stomach and I carry the mixed feeling all the way up to Montmartre, where I aimlessly wander around the department store Tati for forty minutes.

The shop is like an upmarket Festi Bazar but more organised, with junk of all kinds over two wondrous levels. I touch things, gaze at things, consider underpants and soap dishes, pick up a small wicker basket and buy it. A steady stream of lust pumps through my veins, like the druggy feeling of a first crush. I want to keep the feeling in my chest as long as possible, so to stall myself from calling back I walk out of Tati and up a cobblestoned street, where I discover a sprawling indoor fabric market called the Marché Saint-Pierre and spend an hour swimming through taffetas and silks and sequins.

The sun is going down over the railway tracks in the boulevard Barbès when I finally hit redial. Adrien answers with his chocolate voice and we try to make small talk, but I keep talking over him when he goes to say something and then he does the same to me. I manage to ask if he wants to meet for a drink. He says he's working until eight. I say eight's not too late. But he suggests we meet instead on Sunday for a *balade au Louvre*.

'*Disons* fifteen o'clock.'

A Sunday walk around the Louvre? It's only Tuesday! My skin pinches with the wait ahead.

But suddenly it's Sunday and I'm tearing my room to shreds trying to find the right thing to wear. Day *balade* at the Louvre: not formal, but where will we end up? I settle on the trusty black top with the open back and a pair of black jeans. Mum's coat. A smear of Kiki's green eyeshadow that she says looks better on me.

I wait for him beside the inverted glass pyramid in the Carrousel du Louvre, trying not to eat the inside of my mouth. I love that, instead of somewhere dark and intimate, he arranged to meet me beside a great big overpopulated upside-down shard of light. The sky outside, reflected through the glass, is a deep, freezing grey.

Will it snow? They say it doesn't snow every winter in Paris but I dream of seeing it in real life for the first time.

As I'm enjoying an image of Adrien in front of a log fire he appears in front of me, all eyes and hair and gloves and wool. He kisses me on both cheeks and gives an additional arm squeeze, which fuels my electric charge.

He's forgotten that the first Sunday of the month is free, so there's a queue all the way out to the rue de Rivoli. He suggests we ditch the museum and go to Le Marly, and I say, '*Bon!*', though I have no clue what Le Marly is.

He leads me through a secret door and out into the Louvre courtyard, which is veiled in mist. It's empty and quiet due to the cold and he takes my hand and guides me up the steps of an opulent old restaurant. Inside, the place is loud and cosy and bustling. Adrien suggests we sit outside, where we'll have the terrace to ourselves. I know the cold may kill me but I agree – maybe he'll put me under his big warm jacket. I need the Ladies first, so I walk through the warmly lit room, past decadent men and women and pedigree dogs on velvet chairs beneath chandeliers to the bathroom, where an elderly lady smiles at me as the hand dryer splits patches of mink in her coat. I can see the dead animal skin underneath. I wonder if I'll wear fur now, now that I'm a meat-eater, a blood-guzzler, a baby-deer-killer, Satan. Vegie girl in her Room of Good feels far, far away. I piss violently and feel hot blood course through my veins. Life is fucking good. The old lady's perfume is still in the room as I wash my hands and I breathe it in, rich and long – I will be as vile as her, fur or no.

Back outside I need that fur more than ever. Adrien has ordered two café crèmes, which puff their hotness away into the air, leaving but a trace for my insides that need it so badly. The scene is a painting, and I try to forget the petty limitations of the body, taking in every little bit. As I can't relax in the cold, every moment is alive, all is magnified. The top of the glass pyramid glows in the middle of the vast, empty courtyard in front of us. We sit close, but not too close. His shoulders are up and he has one hand in his warm pocket, cigarette in the knuckles of the other. He smiles at me as he raises his cup to his lips. I try to talk but I just keep stammering, so I stop talking and so does he. We sit smoking and watching the tiny birds hop across the balcony near our table. I have no intention of complaining about being cold.

Just as I'm starting to freeze solid, Adrien pays the bill and we walk out along the rue de Rivoli towards the Palais Royal, past the beaded sculpture I sat next to on my first day in Paris six years ago. I don't know why I thought it was an octopus; it's more like an exotic crown or a headdress. I would like to stop and tell Adrien about that day but it's too cold, and he wants to show me the *Colonnes de Buren*, a series of striped columns of different heights poking up from the ground. In the low afternoon light it looks like a field of poker chips. He explains the story of the columns but I can't understand him, so I just nod and *ah* appreciatively. He leads me around the gardens and through the arcades of the Palais Royal, telling me about the history of kings and queens, and showing me the beautiful antique shops and fashion boutiques and fancy restaurants. We stop outside a sumptuous old restaurant called Le Grand Véfour.

'We are not going here,' he says, pointing at the menu price. One day, he tells me, when he is rich, he'll bring me. I note the use of the future tense.

He notices that I'm turning blue so he says, 'Come with me,' and we march soldier-like over to the Marais and step into the first place we see. Perhaps it's somewhere he knows but I don't think so – I can't imagine him frequenting a loud and touristy Spanish bar like this. He goes to the bathroom and I order the first thing that comes into my head: a litre of sangria. It's definitely the wrong choice for a winter tête-à-tête but I don't care: I need to smash the barriers between us, culture, language, sex. He raises his eyebrows when he returns to the table, then pours us both tall glasses and we clink them.

Sure enough, the lower the level of sangria in the jug, the lower the barrier between us.

We start saying things in mixed language.

He says I have beautiful eyes.

I tell him he has beautiful hands.

I go to reach out for one but a bartender approaches our table – he needs to open the trapdoor under my seat so he can go downstairs for ice. I stand up and pull my chair around to Adrien's side. The bar is now crowded. He stands. We are close, but at an awkward angle. I can smell his musky perfume and see dark hairs sprouting from under his top button.

Bam – the man shuts the trapdoor and stands smiling at us, swinging the ice bucket onto his head. '*Ah, l'amour.*'

Adrien's phone rings and he takes it outside. His jaw clenches and his entire expression changes as he talks to the person on the other end. When he comes back in his entire face is flushed.

'I have to go,' he says, sitting back down. 'My mother she call me – *ma grand-mère*, she is here from the ... *campagne*. She is old. I am sorry. I must return.'

'*Ça va*,' I reply, masking my disappointment. 'We can see each other next week.'

'I walk you to the métro.'

Outside, the cold is like being stabbed in the stomach. I grab his arm without thinking – it's life or death – and he grabs mine back. Finally, we're touching. We walk, huddled together, past the Hôtel de Ville, where an ice-skating rink has been set up, the ghoulish silhouettes of skaters dancing against its looming façade.

He holds me a fraction tighter as we cross the street to the Place du Châtelet. The two ancient theatres cast their shadows across the lamplit square, and the angel atop the fountain sculpture reaches her wreaths high into the night sky. Then, just as I stop to admire the beauty of it all, he turns and kisses me, like a character in an old black-and-white photograph, as snow, on cue, feathers down upon our heads.

Narnia

I wake to a bizarre stillness. It's silent outside. No kids in the park. No early-morning traffic. The world feels paused. I know this feeling.

The morning after the night Mum died I woke in our old living room on a raft of cushions. Relatives were scattered around me on couches and blow-up mattresses. I'd forgotten for a moment what had happened. As I realised where I was, the most familiar place on earth, it seemed as if I were waking on a new planet. The air was different. It was as though the molecular structure of the air had shifted overnight. I lay breathing on the cushions, trying to calm myself.

Now I lie in my bed in the Récollets with the same sick feeling. What has happened this time?

The phone rings beside me. I grab it.

'Have you seen it?' says Kiki.

'Is it the end of days?'

She suppresses a laugh. 'Go look out the window.'

I sit up on the bed for a moment, then walk carefully downstairs and pull back the curtains. What I see takes my breath away.

Narnia.

'I know,' says Kiki, hearing my sharp intake of breath.

The park is a fairyland of white. The trees are marshmallows, the buildings wedding cakes. There is no dirt, no rubbish, no people, no dogs, no rushing, no yelling, no bouncing balls. The world has been erased overnight, replaced by sugar candy.

'The Seine is a magical land,' says Kiki.

'It can't be real.'

'It's real.'

'I've never seen anything like it.'

'Because you've never seen snow.'

'I'm going out!'

I hang up and throw on all the clothes I can find and run down to the park. Some kids have arrived and are playing with little plastic sleds and snowballs. I run back upstairs and drag Miru away from his breakfast and down into the Récollets courtyard.

'*La neige!*' he says and throws himself into it. He is excited, but not as much as me. We throw snowballs at each other. One hits me hard in the face and it hurts, but I laugh, tears streaming down my cheeks. Miru flops on his back and moves his arms and legs to make an angel and I do the same.

The streets are slushy by the time I head to school, and I slip and slide my way down the Faubourg-Saint-Denis, wrong to have thought my sneakers would grip. Everyone in class from a hot climate has the same stupid grin on their face. We spend time learning to mime the different speeds of ice-skating, lowering our bodies and faces closer to the ground as we pick up speed, at first staying on the spot then gliding around the room. Ju-Yong says mine is good and gets everyone to stop and watch. I don't know why, I've only ever ice-skated before in my head. In the change room later, Marie-France tells me about a Marcel Marceau scene where he mimes walking up a staircase, showing himself getting higher and higher using only his regard and the angle of his arm. She tells me to come over and watch it one day and I say I will. Damn that Marie-France, she's not even an arsehole.

I'm practising a skating movement in my room that evening, kicking the walls as I push faster and faster, when Adrien calls. In our stilted way we share a mostly French conversation that goes something like this:

'*Allo Jayne?*'

'*Oui?*' (Of course I know it's him but I'll pretend I don't.)

'*C'est Adrien.*' (He knows I'm faking that I don't know it's him, but he'll go along with it.)

'*Oui. Adrien! Bonsoir.*' (I still can't stop saying *oui* on telephone calls.)

'I just finish work. I'm *fatigué*. I'm go home.' (Want to ask me over?)

'*Oui.*' (Ohmygod.)

'I have not disturb you, I hope.' (This is terrible.)

'No, not at all. I'm … brushing my teeth.' (I love the sound of your voice, but not being able to talk properly is making me feel naked, and not in a good way.)

A great big pause.

'Euhhh,' I say. 'Did you see the snow today?' (One day I will lie in bed with you and watch the snow fall outside our window.)

'Yes. I love the snow.'

'I thought the world was dead!'

'That is funny. Okay, I go now.'

'Okay, *oui.*'

'*Je t'embrasse.*'

'*Je t'embrasse …*'

Later, in bed, I send him a message saying thanks for calling and that I'm waiting with *interest*, not *impatience*, to see him again, because Laurent told me that was the less desperate way to express it. He doesn't reply until I'm almost asleep, with a message I have to read over and over:

Ta présence est agréable tout comme ton absence est regrettable.

My presence is agreeable as much as my absence is regrettable? He is regrettable that I am absent from his presence? His place? I haven't seen it yet. Or is he calling it off? And feeling regretful? Should I have invited him over?

This language thing is exasperating. And enticing. Love talk is tantalising enough in my own language, let alone the long hours one can spend deducing what on earth a Frenchman means.

Night Butterfly

'How do you say stapler?' asks Kiki. We are hunched over a table near the window at Chez Jeannette. Our coffees are down to the grainy bits.

'*Agrafeuse*,' I say, exhaling smoke away from her. 'As in *agrafes* – staples.'

'Aggerfuse.'

'No *agra-feuse*. Think agro furs.'

'What about lightbulbs? I need screwy ones.'

'*Ampoules*, but I don't know screwy, you'll have to mime.'

My phone rings as I am miming the lightbulb turn and I show Kiki the caller. She raises her eyebrows twice and coughs, turning to look out the window at a couple having an argument.

Adrien talks in his syrupy murmur and I say *oui* a few times and hang up, flushed.

'The Frenchman is in the 10th for a casting. He wants to come to my place.'

'Ooh la la.'

'He says he's *in* Paris,' I wonder aloud. 'But he says *dans*. I always thought you said *à Paris*, not *dans Paris*. I thought *dans* meant literally being inside something.'

'Maybe he wants to get *dans* you.'

'Maybe,' I say, examining the grit in my coffee cup. 'No,' I realise, looking up at her. 'I've got my period.'

Kiki considers this, then shrugs. 'So what?'

I sprint home wondering if it *is* the moment for him to get *dans* me. It would make for an awkward first time. No, I decide, it's been this long, we should save it.

I shower and change and run down to the Gare de l'Est, but he is not at the little exit in front of the restaurants so I run across to the big exit, but he isn't there either. I ring him and he is at the little exit, standing in front of the Indiana Café, smoking a cigarette. He kisses me intensely on the lips.

'*Comment ça va?*' he asks once we've pulled away, and I say fine thanks and ask how the audition went. He says it was a casting, not an audition, which is slightly different, but he got the job. It's a magazine shoot for a sportswear editorial – modelling but kind of acting, he tells me. Anyway, it's a little bit of money. He's wearing the long black woollen coat from that first night in Martine's doorway and his hair is neat and brushed. I lead him across the traffic to the big white convent and the big iron gates.

'*Waouh!*' he says, looking up and around him at the arcades and tall stone walls with their white-shuttered windows. He knows the building but didn't know what it was.

I tell him about the monks and the hospital and the Angels of the Récollets. He listens in silence as I lead him up to the second floor. In the corridor outside my door we stand for a moment, watching the insane traffic outside the Gare de l'Est. He notices the postcard of the stuffed koala I've stuck on my door and laughs, reminding me that they scratch.

'Not that one,' I say, and put my key in the lock, heart pounding. Cramps thud in my belly.

My studio is messy but the lights are dim. He sits on the Louis XIV chair and I sit on a plastic chair and we drink vanilla tea. I wish I had beer. He is fascinated by how I came to have a residency here and I tell him about the mysterious scholarship and the single email to the embassy and about the mothership near the Place du Colonel-Fabien, where every month they give me a pile of cash to cover living expenses. I still go along expecting the bubble to burst and for them to arrest me and send me home. He tells me I must have sent the email at just the right time.

We lean out the window and smoke, though it's fine to smoke inside. The limbs of the chestnut tree are completely bare now and I point to where we can just see the water of the canal through the park. As we shut the windows, something flies past my face, giving me a fright.

'What was that?' I ask.

'A *papillon de nuit*,' he says, going to look at a moth that has landed on the wall.

'Is that the word for moth? Night butterfly?'

I go and stand by him, looking closely at the moth. It has silvery patterns on its wings. I reach out to touch it and it flies off towards the ceiling.

He turns to me. 'Shall we part?'

We walk side by side down the rue des Récollets towards the canal. As we approach a bar called L'Atmosphère on the banks of the canal he says, 'You know why this bar it's call itself L'Atmosphère?'

'No,' I say, looking up at him.

'You see this bridge there?' He points to the pretty wooden bridge stretched over the dark canal. It's painted green and two men are kissing at the top of it, amidst the naked limbs of the gnarled winter trees. 'You know the film *Hôtel du Nord*?'

I don't.

'Well, inside this film, Arletty, she stand on this bridge and she is crying, "*Atmosphère, Atmosphère, est-ce que je n'ai pas d'atmosphère?*" Édith Piaf she sing in this film too.'

I don't understand why someone would ask, 'Do I have no atmosphere?' and it is one of those annoying moments when I'm not sure what I've understood. How can you trust your comprehension when there are so many senses to so many words, and so many expressions with all sorts of meanings? Adrien is painting pictures in my head. I'll need better French if I'm going to go out with Frenchmen, I decide.

But if I do make the jump to French, can I keep the image of Édith Piaf standing on the Bridge of Atmosphere singing out into the night, and some lady wanting atmosphere?

Inside, L'Atmosphère is so smoky it stings my eyes and I smoke several cigarettes in a row because I might as well. It also gives me something to do with my hands. It's dinnertime and the restaurant is full of people eating foie gras and steak tartare, clinking and murmuring and chewing. There are no seats left so Adrien grabs two from outside that are so cold they pinch my derrière as we sit at a wobbly table near the door. We drink two *demis* each and talk of politics and jobs and weather and traffic and the 10th arrondissement and food.

'Why you no eating meat before?' he asks.

'Oh, many reasons. The taste. Also, I figured if I can't bring myself to kill an animal myself, then I shouldn't eat one. And it's bad for the planet.'

'But good for the taste,' he says. 'You like it now?'

'I have a taste for it now. I've changed. I could kill a cow. Have you ever killed a cow?'

'I have kill a chicken. And goat. Oh – lots of things. You change?'

'I feel different recently. Rawer.'

'Roar?'

'Raw,' I say. 'Umm … bloody.'

'Bloody! Bloody 'ell, mate!' Adrien says, in a Crocodile Dundee way.

'*Zut!*' I say.

He takes a swig of his beer. 'Do you 'aving the sister and brother? What is your family?'

'I have two brothers and a sister. What about you?'

'Just a mother. I am boy unique.'

'You certainly are!' I joke and he smiles, though I know he doesn't get it. He stubs out his cigarette.

'So, your parents split up?'

'I never know him. I know he is half Egyptian. He pay for me to go to a – how do you say – boy school that cost lot of moneys, but that is all. He call me one time, on my eight birthday. Very strange. He and my mother they were very young – he just my father because he make me, nothing else. I am have a lot of fathers.' He laughs. 'And you?' he asks. 'Your parents are together?'

I find myself nodding. I suppose in a way they are. It feels too heavy to tell him anything more right now.

'Are you angry?' he smiles.

Yes. I am so angry I don't know how to begin. But he means hungry, and I say, '*Oui*. Starving.'

We walk out into the freezing night and wander tipsy up the cobblestoned laneways of the canal to the Cambodian restaurant on the avenue Richerand. It's nine o'clock and the restaurant is *complet*, ending our idea of a cosy meal. The little Cambodian lady suggests takeaway, so we order bobuns and wait in the cold by an outdoor table with a vase of frozen flowers on it. An old man wearing an outfit covered in navy glitter tips his hat as he walks past us. He has a silvery moon painted on his forehead and long painted silver shoes that curl up at the ends like moons too. He enters the restaurant and begins performing magic tricks for the clientele.

'When I see magic tricks,' I tell Adrien, 'I believe them.'

'Why not?' he says.

'Tell me what you think of this,' I say. 'I had a penny once. When I came here as an au pair. It was on a string – my sister had put a hole in it. And then one day the penny was gone but the string wasn't broken. What do you think happened to the penny?'

He asks, in French, 'What happened to you before the penny disappeared?'

'I'd just found a job and a place to live, a *chambre de bonne*.'

'So it's clear. The penny wasn't needed anymore.'

I like Adrien's theory. I'm sure drunk Kevin who gave it to me would agree.

'If,' Adrien adds, 'it was there to begin with.'

'Good point.'

The magician performs something low over a table and people clap and cheer. The scene inside the restaurant is warm and inviting, intensifying the cold outside. But I'm fine being out here. Adrien warms me from behind with his coat. His breath on my neck makes me tingle.

'Why don't you stay at my place tonight?' I mumble. 'I don't mean … In fact I'm *indisposed*, I just … thought we could spend the night together.'

'It is possible,' he says.

My studio room is warm and the dinner tasty and the Chinese beer relaxing, and when we're full we lie on our backs on the floor watching clouds puff past the window.

'Try to imagine it's us moving and not the clouds,' he says in French.

The idea is great but makes me dizzy and I have to sit up. He sits up too and laughs. The kissing begins, restrained and gentle at first, then more urgent. He pulls me closer to him. I curse with all my might the monthly curse.

'Want to see E.T.?' I ask, as things heat up. 'He lives in my room.' I lead him upstairs to the mezzanine and lie on the bed, pointing at the old beam running across the ceiling.

'Can you find him?' I ask.

'Where *eez* 'e?' He looks around the room and gives up, flopping beside me on the bed. He's looking straight at E.T. but doesn't realise it. I stand on the bed and point out the curls in the wood for eyes, the indent for a nose, the lines of his alien forehead.

Adrien cocks his head. 'Mmm,' he says. He can't see him yet.

We kiss again for a long while.

'We should sleep,' I say.

'I'll put myself *en caleçon*,' he says, beginning to undress. His body, until now obscured under so much wool and denim, is revealed to me part by part. His frame is smaller than I imagined, more athletic, and he has very long arms with thick, ropey veins protruding all the way from the tops of his shoulders to the tips of his big butcher fingers on his big butcher hands. His skin has tiny white hairs all over it and he has little freckles on his back and shoulders. A welcome-mat of dark hair trails down to his stomach, disappearing at his bellybutton to reappear and lead down behind his *caleçon*, which I now know means underpants. There is a gruesome scar on his right inner thigh, which he tries to cover with his hand.

I touch his hand and move it away.

'It so ugly,' he says.

It really is ugly, and so beautiful, like strawberry and vanilla ice-cream frozen mid-churn.

'I fall from my *moto*.'

'Does it hurt?'

'*Non*, it's just feel strange.'

I touch it lightly.

'It's feel nice when you touch the borders.' He lies back on the bed. I strip down to my knickers, mortified that we are doing this tonight, even more so because I have the terrible undies on that I reserve for this time of the month. I angle myself so he won't notice.

'Oh! I see him!' Adrien exclaims, pointing at E.T. And I am on him.

He kisses me hard and I nibble my way down his chest and stomach. I don't want to go down on him but I feel like I should – I have to do *something*. Should I ask him? Or just do it? The lights are on. I don't want to make him uncomfortable. Is it too soon? I touch his *caleçon*; a thousand thoughts collide in my mouth and I say, 'Is there something …? Could I …? There is something I could … do.'

But he doesn't understand me. I decide to just go for it. He seems nervous but also to be enjoying it. Then he grabs my head.

'*Arrête*, stop, *non, non Jayne*.'

I look up, confused.

'I am too … *excité*.'

'Good!' I resume, but his hand comes back, stronger this time.

'*Non, non, arrête!*'

I smile and continue – I'm going for gold when he wrenches my head away and roars, '*Pleeease!*'

But it's too late. He has spurted across the room, slashing the painting Miru did of me as the serpent girl, sticky-taped to the wall.

'*Pourquoi?*' he whimpers from under his hands, which are firmly clamped across his face. 'What were you doing? *Ça me gênait ... ça me gênait ...*'

Now I'm worried, as I think *gêner* means to be annoyed, and also shocked: doesn't every man like that?

'It was too good, I couldn't hold on!' he moans, peeling his hands away from his blushed, glistening face.

'I didn't want you to hold on!'

'*Oh mon dieu.*' He rolls over onto his side.

I put my face in the top of his back and slide my hand onto the centre of his chest. 'I'm sorry, I really wanted you. I couldn't have sex so ... I didn't mean to upset you.'

'You did not have to do that.'

'But I wanted to! You didn't like it?'

'Yes I liked it,' he says.

'What then? You were worried about *me*?'

I suppose I wouldn't have wanted to be gone down upon on our first go. But that's me. I thought all men loved it, any time, in any circumstance.

'I'm sorry I made you feel weird,' I say.

'It's okay.' He rolls back towards me with soft eyes, then covers his face with his hands again and makes a moaning sound. When he takes his hands away he's smiling. We laugh.

'You're sensitive, aren't you?' I say, tracing his face with my finger.

'*Tu me perces à jour,*' he says.

'What does that mean?'

'Nothing, it does not matter.'

I threaten to go down and look it up on the internet, so he explains that it's like someone putting a hole in you so the daylight can be seen shining through from behind. I don't know if this means I've hurt him, or exposed him, or drilled through him, or if it's something positive. From his soft face I assume it's nothing terrible. He moves me onto my back and explores all the available parts of my body, complimenting each as he goes, in his language. When he arrives at my centre, he places his warm hand right on the most tender part of my lower belly and holds it there until the pain subsides. A glimmer of moonlight catches his forehead, the ends of his eyelashes. Eventually he rolls over and falls asleep.

The morning birds start to chirp in the park. I look at E.T. The moth, perhaps the one from before, rotates on the ceiling above him, flicking its wings and circling before returning to stillness. I change places with the moth and look back at us on the bed, me starfished in underpants, earthy, hair wild over the sheets. Adrien, naked, dark hair on the white pillow. The image is so sexy I want to fly down and fuck us both.

I swap back. Now I'm me again, looking up at the moth. In English, so banal. A plain old moth. In French, a night butterfly. An exotic nocturnal explorer.

Old You

The Barrio Latino is smoky, loud, and packed with glitzy women and arse-grabbing men in business suits. Kiki squeezes my wrist hard as we move past the bouncers. But she owes me one after Martine's party, even if it was a success.

'One hour, promise,' I shout in her ear. I don't want to be here either. I want to be in Adrien's bed with my good undies on. Off. But he is away on the shoot for two days. A fortunate thing because I'm not sure how I would explain that I am meeting up with Jack's friends.

James, Wil and Patrick are seated at a private table up the back, drunk amongst the remnants of dessert. My heart leaps at the sight of their familiar faces. It wasn't long ago we were drinking beers together at my farewell, recovering the next day in Jack's backyard. That day I had felt for the first time a desire not to leave, to stay in that familiar place, marry Jack, find a way to make it all okay.

You're just going to run off with some Frenchman.

The three men look out of place in their grungy shirts and jeans, beards, and hair reminiscent of 1970s pop-rock bands. James actually is a musician and has been shooting a film clip in Paris with his band. Wil and Pat have been in London on tour, acting in a play. They stand and cheer as we arrive and ply us immediately with champagne, cake and a cannon of questions: 'Do you like it here?' 'How's your

French?' 'Do you like the French?' 'Are you coming home for Christmas?' 'Are you ever coming home?'

I down two glasses of champagne to make the questions easier, and fire a whole heap back to divert their attention from me. They're happy to be in Paris, in a nonchalant kind of way. I can't imagine feeling a breath of nonchalance at any single moment spent in Paris, and wonder what it would be like to not feel so excited all the time. Are they feeling it but can hide it better? I feel a warmth rise in me, both from the champagne and the familiarity of these boys I know well, but not too well.

After more champagne and some shots of something indecipherable we go to the dance floor to throw our bodies around to the Latino-techno fusion. James does a strange, bendy, rubber-man dance and Wil does a four-step on repeat. Their dancing is ironic, like their outfits. They could not look less Parisian. Ironic fashion and behaviour is not something I have seen here at all.

A wiggly worm of a man in tight leather pants with a visible boner works his way into my rear and starts gyrating, putting his hands on my hips, which makes me gasp and jump and fall on Kiki in fits of hysterical repulsion. This only entices him more and he comes back for seconds before James gives him a look that sends him dancing madly away.

Hours later we stumble to a darkened bar on the corner of the rue de Lappe, full of velvet furniture and old lamps. The boys keep ordering drinks until the dusty night sky starts turning blue. Wil and James needle me with drunken questions about men in Paris, on a clear mission to get information for Jack. My wingman is long gone, the Cité walking distance away, but it's still only five am and I have at least half an hour until the first métro. I do my best to dodge the questions.

'How long are you here again?' I ask Wil, propping my head up with my hand. Patrick has fallen asleep on a chaise longue.

'Another week,' says Wil.

'It's my birthday on Wednesday. I'm having a dinner. You'll all have to come.'

'Long as you don't make us eat frogs' legs,' says James, swirling his ice cubes.

A large group of women roll in from what looks like a hen's night and the boys fire up. I kiss them goodbye and snake my way through the calm, early-morning streets to the métro, drunken me managing to beat down the speck of sober me who is saying, Jesus, you idiot, you invited the Frenchman to your birthday dinner, how is *that* going to work? Ah, peaceful drunk me, with lovely soft brain, riding the warm carriage home with all the grey morning faces, to pass out on my floor like someone who's just spent a month in the desert.

Adrien is back for an evening but has to leave at five the next morning for his last day of shooting, so we arrange to see each other for dinner. We meet at the place we first kissed, and, though it's freezing outside again, I begin to sweat as I run from rehearsal at Marie-France's near Bastille. I'm running late but slow down to breathe and collect myself as I approach Châtelet.

As I cross into the square, dark amongst the golden lights and bustle of the theatres, I see him. He sees me, and I see him seeing me but he pretends he hasn't seen me. I pretend not to have seen that he saw me. I walk up and tap on his shoulder and he acts surprised and we kiss awkwardly, he going central, me towards his cheek. Then we kiss again, longer, and my shoulders relax. Now I know what's under all those layers I want to wriggle my hands up there and touch his warm skin, but I don't. I need to keep my head on.

We hold hands as we walk, but it doesn't feel right so we let go. The Hôtel de Ville looks hauntingly beautiful against the almost black sky, and it thrills me how such an imposing and vast building can also seem so warm and welcoming. But anywhere is calmer right now than my own insides. I chew frantically at the inside of my mouth, though I keep telling myself to stop. We make small talk about snow and I use some of the vocab I've learnt from school and local discussions. Things are more comfortable when we speak in French, so I keep speaking it, flipping back to English when I don't have the words for something.

Kiki suggested we try Le Bûcheron on the rue de Rivoli, as it's warm, cheap and delicious. As we approach, the restaurant looks so dim inside we think it's closed, but a door opens and a man ushers us to a table down the back. Adrien gestures for me to take the cushioned banquette.

He orders wine and my stomach tightens further at the thought of bringing up Jack or anything from home at this early stage. Ah, why had I let Kiki convince me to have a birthday dinner in the first place?

I try to order the most elegant thing on the menu, but it's a pasta restaurant and my tagliatelle is impossible to eat without slurping it all over my face. I can't digest anything anyway, so I pick around my plate as we discuss theatre, work, *n'importe quoi*. This is my favourite new expression – 'nothing of import'. I also suddenly know how to use *il faut* in a sentence, and it makes sense to me in a peculiar, physical way – I can't translate it into English words, but I know it. This is a strange phenomenon and tells me that a French part of me is opening up that I didn't know was there. It makes me wonder if all languages live inside of us and we just have to unlock them. How else is it possible to understand and express something without being able to translate it into your native tongue?

The conversation keeps spurting like diarrhoea as I spout *n'importe quoi* and avoid bringing up what I know I should, blabbing all sorts of nonsense about knowing what kind of actor you want to be and never compromising, etc, etc. I don't *have* to tell him anything – I could wing my birthday and let Adrien and Jack's friends just meet. But it feels mean for Adrien not to know who they are. It's okay if the boys go running back to Jack and tell him about Adrien – we agreed we would see other people – though it would be less cowardly if I told Jack first. But what's the point in telling Jack before I'm sure it's serious? It may not last. The boys are unpredictable, especially after a few drinks. Oh god. How did things get so complicated so quickly?

Le Bûcheron is yet another restaurant with toilets *à la turque*, and though my aim is good I feel the warmth of my own piss hitting my stockinged ankle. Then I bump my head really hard on the low ceiling of the stairwell as I walk up, and conclude that this is not my night. *Just tell him.*

I slide back into my seat. 'I should tell you something.'

He looks relieved, like he knew something was up. Or perhaps it's my correct use of tenses.

'*Oui?*'

I scramble for the words and he encourages me to just come out and say it, but trying to explain this sort of thing is hard enough in my own language.

I manage something like: 'It's nothing really, it's just that I *had* something before I came over here. A someone. An Australian. It was. He was. We were … It was complicated.'

Oh god, should I tell him about Mum too? Oh god. No no no.

'So. When I came to Paris we decided to stop things and be free. Well, I decided. So. That, well. Anyway. I wanted to let you know about him, because a few of his friends are coming to my birthday dinner next week. I wanted to be honest with you because I like you. Like I said. Did I say that? Sorry. It really doesn't make any difference to us, it's nothing.'

He smiles and the awkwardness lifts completely away. It feels like we know each other a bit better too. His eyes are still and calm.

'Well, it clearly makes a difference to you. Do you still want me to come to the dinner? It's okay if I don't come.'

'No, no, of course I want you to come, I just wanted you to be aware who they are.'

He tells me he appreciates my honesty, and that he's glad I got it off my chest. I tell him I feel much better and he takes my hand and gives me a stabbing look. Then he orders the tiramisu.

We kiss in an alcove outside the restaurant, long and steamy. The thick layers of clothes add a bodice-era erotic charge to it all. I understand the game now, and this time it's me who pulls back and says goodbye. He walks away with a lingering look and I walk in the other direction, towards Kiki's, to tell her everything.

The rue de Pont Louis-Phillippe, between Kiki's and the rue de Rivoli, has become my favourite street, with shops selling old quills and ink and handmade paper and musical instruments. There is a church on the street and there must be a convent, because I often see nuns out walking in their demure blue and white. I nod to them, as though living in the Récollets I have something in common with them. When I relay this feeling to Kiki she smiles sweetly, eyes filling with water as she tries not to laugh. Then I tell her about the head job, to which she replies, 'Jesus. Glad it wasn't my artwork on the wall.' She thinks it's cute that I told Adrien about Jack's friends, but that I didn't need to. Then she goes back to the documentary she's been watching about Simone de Beauvoir, as I make us cups of tea.

The show is on French TV, so she can't rewind, but we keep watching the rest of it together. When it's over she gets out some red nail polish to paint her nails in short red squares, like the hands of the actress who portrayed Simone.

'"One is not born a woman,"' I say to her, translating one of de Beauvoir's major lines in the documentary. '"One becomes a woman." What a load of shit.'

'You don't think that's true?' says Kiki.

'I don't know. What if you don't want to become one?'

'I do,' says Kiki.

'I want to become a man.'

'No you don't,' says Kiki. 'You want little red Simone de Beauvoir nails.'

I do want little red Simone de Beauvoir nails. I take off my socks and start painting my toenails. Mum used to do hers in red like this. When she was little she wasn't allowed to, so she painted her doll Sally's red. Mum had so much weight on her shoulders, though she never showed it. I don't think I could do what she did, and smile, as she did, raise four kids, keep a clean house, be pleasant and graceful and beautiful and giving, all the time, to everyone else.

'Why toes?' asks Kiki.

'I can't do fingers – school.'

'Oh yeah.'

Having the red toes under my shoes feels good. A secret piece of woman hidden down beneath the fluff.

On the way home from the bank on Wednesday afternoon the train stops short between Châtelet and Les Halles because of a suspicious package. It's already past six and people are coming to my place at seven for *apéro* before the dinner. The train is crowded and a Latino musician blows an out-of-key trumpet in my face. There is no escape: the doors are jammed shut between the stations. I try not to huff and shift from foot to foot, there's no point.

An actor should be able to see the sea in the métro, says Angela in my head. Not just act that he sees the sea, she explained, but truly see the sea. I try to do this, but all I can see is a tide of bodies rammed up against each other, tired, blank, angry; a drunk woman passed out on two fold-down seats. The smell of fresh urine hits my nostrils and I ignore it as I reach for a space on the sweaty pole; there's nothing to be gained in registering smells. If you do you'll die at the first encounter of the Les Halles métro warren: the never-changing air of fresh human shit. When I was here as an au pair, I would look around, shocked, to see who else had noticed. Nobody. Now I'm as deadpan as the others. I am becoming Parisian. Here I am, an apprentice Parisian standing in this carriage in which somebody just pissed themselves, and sea water is flooding in, frothing and swirling around our ankles, rising, and we are going under, down and down to the coral and sea creatures, through the clear salty water. I am seeing it, the pissy sea in the métro. A whale swims past. Jacques Lecoq laughs and swims with us all. We arrive at the sandy sea floor with a squeak.

The carriage doors open at the Gare de l'Est.

My studio is a mess, and who knows where everyone will fit. And what on earth should I wear? I decide on the denim skirt and the brown dotty top, which is boring but also just right, and then there's a knock at the door. Thank god it's Kiki, holding a basket of food and one of Norbert's magnums.

'You look amazing!' she says hugging me.

'Still *mademoiselle*?' I ask, tugging at my top.

'Like a beautiful 29-year-old *mademoiselle*.'

'I got *madame*'d yesterday.'

'Hair up or down?'

'Down!'

'That's fucked,' she says. 'You must be right on the cusp.'

In her basket is everything you use to cook a basic dhal. She says she'll teach me. It's one of the most considerate gifts I've ever received – an education in a basket. Possibly inspired by my call to her last week asking how to boil an egg.

She pours vodka into two coffee cups and hands me one. 'Get that in ya.'

I down it and say, 'I want Adrien's arrival to be well timed.'

'I'll talk to him, don't worry.'

Another knock at the door: James, Patrick and Wil, each in a scruffy variation of hipster Melburnian. Faye Ohio is next, followed by Ravi Canada.

Kiki puts nuts and olives in a bowl and some chips on a platter and I put thinly sliced meats and cheeses on a board and we all talk and mingle, holding our cups and food up close to our chests. Adrien is last to arrive. He has carefully trimmed stubble and is wearing an embroidered black shirt under his jacket. We kiss in the hallway and he hands me a box of chocolates, an enormous bunch of red roses and a bottle of Roederer champagne. I am embarrassed to be doing the birthday thing when we hardly know each other, and blush at the unfettered romance of the gifts. I hide the roses in the shower, making an excuse about not having a big enough vase, before introducing him around the room.

'Here you go!' shouts Kiki to me, holding the roses in a toilet roll container above her head. 'This will work!' She plonks them right in the middle of the desk where the food is. It might as well be Adrien's and my naked bodies there amongst the hors d'œuvres, but nobody seems to notice. Kiki talks to him for a while in French, then gets shy and moves on to Wil, leaving Adrien alone with the cheese in a sea of Anglophones. Ravi Canada rescues him, then we all walk down the canal to La Marine, the magical restaurant with the fairy-lit windows and mosaic floors and shining brass bar. I can't afford it, but I'll eat dhal for a month.

Meg London and Marc Finland join us there and we eat and drink and I smoke nonstop as my worlds smash together around me. Adrien sits by my side and helps me blow out the candles and lights my cigarettes, one after the other. After dinner he says he has to catch the last train home, kisses me and all the others goodbye, and leaves. I am sad he's gone, but it's easier. There is an interested silence around the table before someone orders a round of cocktails and before I know it I am wildly drunk, and we keep drinking until La Marine closes.

It's icy outside by the canal and some people go home, but Laurent, Faye, Wil, Kiki and I go back to my place and drink Kiki's vodka pommes, though I'm so drunk I can't even taste them, and then she rolls a big strong joint and we laugh and laugh at my ridiculous chair and I eventually pass out cold on a jacket on the floor.

The sound of water boiling in the saucepan wakes me the next morning. Kiki and Wil's feet are beside my head. Kiki is jiggling a teabag.

'Where did you sleep?' I murmur, sitting up.

'Up there,' she says, and Wil looks up at the same time. He smiles. Kiki's a dirty dog.

'Stubble boy is nice,' he says, leaning against the wall with pastry crumbs all over his chin.

I see the time on his watch. 'Fuck!' I yell, pulling on my blacks and running out the door.

Red

My toenails are red and I am dead. Of all the days to forget my ballet shoes I had to choose today, with a pounding hangover. I will be seen as *jolie*. Being pretty at Lecoq is a fate worse than death.

I consider leaving my socks on in the *Grand Salle*, to keep the toenails well hid, but I've seen what happened to Amy Beijing's right hip on these hardwood floors. I can't risk it. So when warm-up begins I take off my socks and pray hard. Oh god, let them not see, and please god, let it not be true that the teachers sit up in their hidden staffroom, high in the rafters, watching us all. If they see my *jolie* nails, I'm sure not to make it through to second year. And I will die if I don't make it through to second year.

Ju-Yong puts us in pairs. We learn to mime paddling a boat, plunging an imaginary oar deep into the water to push us across the pond. Étienne is next to me and points at my toes. *Shut the fuck up*, I say to him with my eyes.

Ju-Yong claps his hands and we start running around the space. He claps and we stop and mime throwing an imaginary net out as far as we can. I'm right at the back of the room, thank goodness. Marie-France has seen my toes and moves in front of me, trying to cover for me. I smile at her and she gives me a serious nod. He claps and we're off again. I avoid the front of the room. *Clap*. Damn, I am dead centre. Ju-Yong points straight at my toes.

'Ah, Jayne. Very beautiful.'

Everyone looks. He lets the silence sit. Bright red nails detract from the idea. It's not about *us*. It's about what we're creating. Painted nails draw attention. They are womanly. And dressed in our blacks, we have no gender, no detail to differentiate us except our drawn, pale faces and varied body shapes.

Once Ju-Yong is satisfied that my face has turned as red as my nails, he claps his hands and the lesson continues.

Later, in neutral mask class, I'm up the back watching, pants pulled down over my feet, when a dumpy Brit called Peter lets out a high squeaky fart in a silent, serious part of the mask journey. The mood is so serious it makes me want to burst with laughter, but I hold it in and run out of school straight afterwards and call Kiki, knowing she'll see the humour in it. She almost does, any fart story is funny to her, but she can't quite picture the solemnity of the deadpan leather mask, the almost meditative silence of the classroom as we watched each actor make their journey over the plain and across the river and up the hill. With our faces covered and only eyeholes to look out of and a small slit to breathe through, our bodies are our only means of expression and each gesture is magnified. It's a weird sensation, both to watch and to wear the mask. The teachers say the mask has a powerful effect on the psyche and can provoke strange dreams.

Kiki tells me the sex with Wil was tops – a straight-up drunk fuck, which she needed because Zahir's meticulous sensitivity has started to become annoying – and asks me to come and see Zahir's play with her tonight, to which I say no because I'm too hungover, but she says I owe her for the happy future with Adrien and also the Barrio Latino, to which I say but you get a happy future with Wil out of that, and she says no, that was just a drunk fuck, to which I say touché. I go home and throw on an outfit with way too many colours in it and run back out to the métro.

The play is extremely good, and very boring. A woman twirls for twenty minutes in a circle of white eggs without getting dizzy while a guy does some jerky dancing next to her, like he's having a fit, and Zahir moves around randomly, speaking Arabic with a grandiose air. Then he takes off his shirt, which makes it all truly wonderful. Zahir is a sort of bald god.

Afterwards the three of us go to a bar shaped like a horseshoe in the Marais. Kiki and I drink beer. Zahir drinks tea and shows me a photo from back in Palestine when he had wild, fuzzy black hair.

'You look so different,' I say.

'As an actor in Palestine I get typecast. So I grow my hair. It help.'

'Really? How?'

'To take focus from my beautiful face,' he says with the utmost solemnity. I see his point.

Kiki asks me to come back to her studio, as she doesn't want to spend the night with Zahir. We lie on the fold-out bed and smoke a joint, watching *Rain Man* dubbed in French. Then we eat miso soup that she's made with vegetables and noodles in it and afterwards she makes hot chocolate with real chocolate and we suck on sweet, juicy clementines.

'Pull my finger,' says Kiki, and her fart is joyful with a little question mark at the end. I cry with laughter into the pillow.

'Farts are very funny,' she says, and lights another joint.

'Why do they so often go unacknowledged?'

'If someone had laughed, then everyone would have.'

'I should have laughed.'

'But then if nobody else laughed it would have been embarrassing.'

'Which I guess is why nobody laughed.'

I get up and go to the window and look out. There has been no snow since Narnia and I've been praying for it to return. It's a clear night and I can see all the way down the river to the top of Notre-Dame.

'I could live here forever and become a Frenchy and have little baby croissants,' I say.

'Not *moi*. I like it here but I would never stay.'

'Everyone at school says the same thing. They can't wait to get back to their own countries.'

'I like Manu, my yoga teacher,' says Kiki. 'He's a Frenchy.'

'There you go – marry him and stay here with me forever and ever.'

'He says *shanti shanti om* at the end of phone calls.'

'You're talking to him on the phone?'

'And in the classes he feels me up.'

'Isn't that illegal? In the yoga law?'

'Nothing is illegal in the yoga law.'

'What about Zahir?'

'I'm bored of Zahir. Can't get it up anymore.'

'He seems pretty turned on by you.'

'I mean me.'

'Oh. With that beautiful dick and all?'

'Yeah. But you know – the pussy knows.'

'Excuse me?'

'The pussy knows. I read it somewhere.'

She yawns and kisses me, going into her little bedroom.

'What does that mean?' I call out, getting under the covers.

'Nothing else matters,' she yells. 'Your pussy knows when it's over.'

'You're completely guided by your pussy? What does she say?'

But Kiki is already doing her lady-snore. I lie awake wondering if my pussy is trustworthy, before falling into a deep sleep.

Kiki is opening the curtains naked when I wake. She has amazing round breasts and a clipped little bushy triangle. Her nipples are pale pink, which is surprising considering her olive complexion and raven hair. Girls' parts, evidently, don't always match their bodies.

Outside it's sunny; November is a constant surprise. She stands amongst the curtains looking out at the sky, the river, the trees, closing her eyes and swaying gently, curves bathed in the cool light. When she opens her eyes and turns she looks almost sad. Then she walks towards the kitchen, picking her nose.

She comes back with coffee and I get up and hug her, looking out at the windows twinkling over on the Île Saint-Louis, excited by the unexpected sun. She serves a comprehensive breakfast involving yesterday's baguette toasted and little jars of yoghurt. As always, her coffee, made in a silver contraption, is delicious. It must be nice to be you, I think, looking after yourself so nicely. When I'm on my own I never bother to do things like make a good coffee. I eat the little toasts from a packet and drink teabag tea. I make a pact to make my life nicer for myself, even when nobody's there.

'Did you sleep well?' I ask.

'Yeah, except for Zahir banging at the door.'

'Wow. I never sleep through anything.'

'His play has been extended! How am I supposed to live my life with all these men wanting to extend their stay?'

'What did you say to him?'

'Fuck off back to Palestine.'

'You didn't.'

'No. He was drunk and ranting – I can't believe you didn't hear.'

'How did you make him go away?'

'I didn't.'

I poke my head around the corner and, sure enough, there is Zahir's beautiful face asleep on her pillow.

Kiki nods. 'Crazy man.'

I somehow make it to school on time and get up to do my impression of a plastic cup toppling off a table. I spent an entire afternoon perfecting this movement, watching a cup fall over and over again. But plastic requires a certain tonicity that I don't have, and mine is floppy and inarticulate.

'Can *anybody* tell what she is?' asks Angela.

'Dirt?'

'Water?'

'Wood?'

'What *are* you?' Angela asks at last.

'A plastic cup,' I squeak.

'For me, it is *caoutchouc*,' Angela says. 'Sit down.'

My plastic looks like rubber. How embarrassing. Angela gives us an exercise in which we wash a T-shirt, then become the T-shirt, then hang ourselves out on the line to dry. After that we practise being paper – small pieces, thick pieces, tissue paper, toilet paper; being scrunched up, torn, thrown. My piece of paper is a letter someone didn't want to read and is thus savagely murdered. Murdering myself feels great. I tear myself to shreds and lie bleeding in strips of my former self. Angela says it was a *bel engagement* but didn't really look like paper. I wonder what it did look like but am too scared to ask. How to find the delicate yet sharp texture of paper? Its flatness and pliability, lightness, fragility, strength. Paper is hard, and I decide that I will practise until I master it.

That night I have a dream. Something smells strange. I'm in Mum and Dad's bathroom with the cough-drop lampshade and the shower door coming off its hinge. The basin reads *Hermitage Shanks* and Dad's Old Spice is on it, beneath the sliding mirror with the tiny groove in it for your fingers. The place is splattered with soap scum. It is too silent.

Something is behind the door. I can't see it but I can feel it. The door is pushing against something soft. I peer behind it, heart racing. It's Mum. She is a pile of yellowing bones. She looks up and holds out a jaundiced arm. Her eyes beg for help. I don't know what to do. In a moment of panic I put the door back in its place. Then I go downstairs. I feel disgusting: I know I should have done something to help her but I just keep moving forward. Relatives are in the kitchen. Mum's sisters, our cousins, Dad, Kate, Alex, Ben. It's a tea party, but sombre. They begin to wonder why Mum's not coming down. I say nothing, guilt deep in my belly. People whisper, 'Where's Annie?'

My uncle bursts into the room. 'She's alive! I found her! She's alive!'

The terrible feeling at having left her is replaced by a searing joy. She's alive! She's alive!

Mum stands on the staircase, radiant. We all stare. She looks at us all, then moves down the stairs into the kitchen. The dishwasher hums. Everyone goes back to the party.

She walks towards me and smiles. She knows I left her there. But everything is okay now.

I wake with the swelling feeling that she's alive. Then the horror as I remember she is dead. The shock is intense, it cuts my breath. I sit up and clutch my knees, breathe, breathe. I won't cry, I don't know where I'll end up if I start. Keep it together. You are here, in Paris. Breathe. Lie back down. Look at E.T. Go to school.

Little Death

Everyone, including Adrien, goes away for the two-week Christmas break, leaving me and Kiki lying around drinking vodka during the day and eating hot things she cooks. On Christmas Day we dress up and walk down the deserted rue du Faubourg-Saint-Denis to the exquisite brasserie Julien, but the lunch menu is exorbitant so we go next door to the Derya Turkish restaurant and share a lamb kebab for ten bucks. Then we walk to Notre-Dame and go inside, which I have never done before, and sit in the back pews listening to a choir of women's voices reverberate around the ceilings, feeling like orphans, but really happy ones. It's dark when we leave, and starting to rain slush, so we run across the bridge to Kiki's place, trying not to slip. I want to stop and look out over the river with all the lights and ripples, but she tugs me on.

I tell her about the Mum dream and she gives me a long warm hug. She doesn't know how to interpret it. Just that perhaps dreaming about her isn't good for me, as my sense of reality is already a bit warped. Perhaps that's why I haven't dreamt of her before, she says – it's too destabilising.

I don't think my sense of reality is warped, I tell her. I just still can't believe she's dead. I have to bite my lip hard then, not to cry.

'I just mean because you're so far away from home you're processing it differently,' she says, hugging me again. 'Here you can just forget it happened.'

The next day, my family calls. It's evening there and they are sitting by a pool. They each ask me about snow. Kate tells me that Jack has a new girlfriend. It's an unexpected kick in the stomach, the frozen image I have of home cracking. I'm relieved not to have to tell him about Adrien. But it still feels like the ground pulling away.

Adrien returns on New Year's Eve and asks me to meet him for dinner at Odéon. As I arrive at the top of the métro stairs I see him standing beside a billboard, talking into his phone. Catching sight of me, he continues his conversation but turns his body around to look at me. The barrier of the person on the phone allows us to look at each other as long as we want, and he holds my gaze until my cheeks turn red and I have to look away and plunge my hands deep into my pockets.

'*Désolé*,' he says after he hangs up, pulling me towards him and kissing my lips then my neck. The fire I've had to dampen inside myself these past weeks takes no time to rekindle. He looks slightly different to how I remembered him – shorter, but still dashing. He is wearing a red silk scarf, which makes him look like someone from a period drama. He leads me through a series of alleyways, past the white stone archways of the Marché Saint-Germain and up the quaint rue Saint-Sulpice, where a fat drop of water falls in my hair. I put my hand out.

'*Il pleure*,' I say.

Adrien laughs. 'That's so cute,' he says. '"It is crying."'

'No, I mean raining. *Il pleure*.'

'*Il pleut*,' he corrects. 'Rain is *pleuvoir*. *Pleurer* it mean to cry. But it's true, because ze sky he is crying.'

He ushers me down a stairwell and into a cosy Italian restaurant. The waiters know him and he orders stuffed mushrooms and simple chilli pasta for us both and we try to eat but the table is electric. Our hands and knees and feet are touching below.

When Adrien pays the bill the waiter calls me a *belle demoiselle*. It feels like the perfect compliment. I do feel *belle*. And *demoiselle* feels like the perfect compromise between *mademoiselle* and its staid alternative.

We walk to a place called the Bar du Marché where a man in overalls and a sailor cap brings mojitos to our tiny table with a candle on it. The air is clammy with body heat and smoke. A strand of my hair falls into the candle and burns. It stinks. Adrien picks up his glass to clink with mine.

'*Joyeuse nouvelle année,*' I say. 'I just realised I have no idea how to say happy new year!'

'*Bonne année.*'

'Good year? That's funny.' We drink the mojitos and then another each and it's only eleven pm but I suggest we take a taxi back to my place. He smiles and grabs my hand beneath the table.

The taxi ride is a flurry of lips and hair.

At the gates of the Récollets, in a rush to get inside, we bump into Lamine, an actor from Mali who lives on the ground floor.

'Jayne! You coming or not?'

I'd forgotten he invited me to his friend's New Year's Eve party.

'Do you want to go?' I ask Adrien. 'Just for a few drinks?'

'*Venez, venez, venez,*' says Lamine, grabbing both our arms. I tell Adrien how Lamine is studying acting at the Conservatoire and the two men chatter past the brasseries of the Gare de l'Est and across into the rue du Faubourg-Saint-Denis and up the rue de Paradis. The streets are full of clutter and noise: it's staggering how different the streets are here compared to the order and cleanliness of the Saint-Germain area we've just come from. It feels good to be back where it's messy and loud.

Lamine's friend Franck lives in a sixth-floor *chambre de bonne* and the tiny space is crammed with sweaty bodies. An arm reaches out to fill our plastic cups with straight rum, as there are no mixers or champagne left. Adrien and I tap cups and I drink mine down as he sips on his. Lamine pulls his T-shirt up and ties it like a bikini, exposing the washboard abs he likes to parade around the Récollets. He spins me around and gyrates at my side as I toss my head back, laughing wildly. Adrien stands in the corner, stiff in all his clothes but smiling amongst the writhing bodies.

People are climbing in and out of Franck's window and after several shots I step up onto the rotting sill and beckon to Adrien. We clamber out and shimmy across a ledge to a tiny step that leads up to an abandoned balcony. He reaches his arm out to protect me. '*Fais attention. C'est hyper dangereux.*'

We step up carefully and turn around. The view over the north of Paris is breathtaking. The balcony is only as wide as us, so we lean back against the building for safety. Though if I have to die, I wouldn't mind slipping off this ramshackle ledge into the night with Adrien. The Sacré-Cœur glows like a meringue on the hill of Montmartre and for the first time I appreciate why the Parisians call it that. Two statues of men – or perhaps women – on chairs look out over the city from the top of the Gare de l'Est. The lights of the Gare du Nord cast an eerie glow over the neighbourhood that lies littered before us like a field of scrap paper. People move about in distant windows, chimneys sprout haphazardly, birds scratch and tap and roost.

A great boom sounds and a series of fireworks lights up the sky. Throughout Paris, shouts and claps and clinks are magnified a millionfold – the whole city is alive at our feet. I squeeze his hand.

'Good year,' I say.

'Good year.'

It's difficult to kiss but we manage it, standing side by side, the tiles behind us rattling as we fumble. A piece chinks off and goes flying into the night. I can feel an erratic move coming on, so I take his hand and we climb back down to the party, and back through the streets to my studio.

I slam my door shut behind us and lean against it suggestively. He puts his heavy hands on hips. 'Shall we go *en haut*?' I say, pointing up to the mezzanine.

'*En haut*,' he says, pressing his body against me, 'is pronounced *ohaw*. No "n".'

The complexity of phrases with no consonant sounds is far less interesting than the inside of his mouth, and the sex against the door is over in minutes. Then we go *en haut* and he is back for more but it goes too long – he goes somewhere else – and I clutch at him until his face turns red and the veins in his forehead pop out and he falls off me, apologising, wet all over.

I feel strange but glad he went for it. It's just the first time.

In the morning I sneak out while he's still asleep to buy croissants from the patisserie, because the *confiserie* and the *traiteur* and the boulangerie are all shut. The woman is cold and I am cold back and she gives me good buttery ones. Then I go to the *épicerie* and buy expensive milk because the *supermarché* is shut too, and when I get home I notice it's out of date and curse the man who sold it to me. I make us both *cafés allongés* instead.

Ça coûte la peau du cul. Ça coûte la peau du cul, I repeat in my head as I climb up to wake him. I heard Étienne say this the other day in an impro about a man buying a car. I think it means 'It costs the skin off your arse.'

I kiss his face lightly and his eyes open. 'Hello, miss,' he says.

'Hello, man.' I put my face against his. 'Your eyelashes are as long as a girl's.' I bat my own against his cheek, then put my eye to his, like Dad used to when we were kids. 'A butterfly kiss,' I say. 'Do you have those?'

'No. A *baiser papillon*?'

'Isn't *baiser* a rude word?'

'*Baiser* on his own mean "fuck", but *un baiser* it's mean a kiss.' He kisses me gently on the nose.

'Confusing!'

'You have to be careful.'

'I bet. *Du café*?'

'Yes please, *papillon*,' he says, climbing down the steps. His hair is rough and sexy. He goes into the bathroom and tames it with water.

'*Ça coûte la peau du cul*,' I say as I pour the coffee.

'Don't pronounce the "l" in *cul*,' Adrien says. '*Mon cu—*.'

'Mon kewww.'

'*C'est ça*. A more polite way is to say, *Ça coûte les yeux de la tête*.'

'It costs the eyes from your head?'

'*Les yeux de la tête, Mistinguett*.'

That's the second time he's called me Mistinguett. I like the way it sounds. I don't know if it's a person or a film title or an old show, but I've seen a giant poster at the back of Le Progrès, in Montmartre, with a woman clutching a flower on a blustery day.

Adrien goes to the window, opens it and breathes in the cold air. There is cheese hanging off the windowsill and he pulls it in like a fish and sniffs it. It stinks so bad I can't keep it inside. I'm sure it's off but he says there is no such thing and licks the ooze from his fingers.

'Is Mistinguett good?' I ask. 'Do you like her?'

'I like *you*,' he replies. '*Papillon fou*. You, crazy butterfly. My mother, she like Mistinguett. She like old music like this. Old *personnages*.'

He eats a grape from the bowl on my table.

'What's your favourite fruit?' I ask him.

'Red berries.'

'What kind of fruit would you say these are?' I ask, putting my hands on the little round protrusions in my T-shirt.

He blushes. '*Des raisins*,' he says, crawling over to me to bite at my shirt. I kiss his greased hair and try to explain to him that raisins in English are small, hard and dry. He looks up and smiles with his eyes closed then puts his head back on my top and his hands up it. My top comes off, then my clothes one by one, and now I'm naked on the cement floor, it's as cold as a morgue, he is over me, fully clothed, and the cold down the back of my body is in such contrast to the warmth of my flesh that I feel everything, and he does all the right things at just the right moments, and also surprises me, and I resist at first and then let myself fall right over the cliff. No wonder they call it a *petite mort*. I just died, hard. We go back upstairs and he dies too and this time he stays with me and his face is not red.

The sky through the window is a deep purplish grey. We lie in silence for a long time and then more questions come. Favourite this, favourite that. First this, first that. His first memory was breastfeeding from a dog. I sit up. No! Yes. When he was born, his mum's dog grew milk, and one day his mother found him beneath her, suckling at her. She rushed to remove him – the dog tried to bite her – and took him to the doctor, who said dog's milk is fine for humans.

'Wow, good to know,' I say.

'*Voilà.*'

He also remembers being on a leash. As a toddler he kept running into traffic and once tried to fly off his mother's fourth-floor balcony.

I tell him my first memory was when my sister, Kate, was born, though I can never be sure what is a real memory and what is just stories and photos.

He says that when his dog died, it was like his mother had died. 'My dog, she is more soft than my mother.'

I consider telling him about my own mother but the moment has passed, so I ask instead, 'Are you afraid of dying?'

'No. Are you?'

'No, but I'm afraid of getting sick.'

'Death is the end of nothing,' he says, adjusting his hair. 'Shall we go for a *promenade* in the Marais?'

It's freezing outside and when I grab my umbrella Adrien laughs. 'It's too cold to rain!' I stand for a moment trying to absorb this concept. He looks me slowly up and down. 'You are going out like zis?'

I am wearing jeans with two pairs of stockings and a pair of woollen socks pulled up under them, two thin jumpers and the leather coat. I'm still adamant about the doodoona.

He takes off his scarf and winds it around and around my neck.

'But what about you?' I ask.

'I am hot blood man.' He lovingly tucks the scarf into the front of my coat. 'Still crazy. You will die. But better.'

It's quiet out in the streets and most of the shops are shut. We have to walk all the way to the rue du Faubourg-du-Temple to find cigarettes and Adrien lights mine between my gloved fingers. The cold burns. A winter flea market sprawls over the pavements of the rue de Bretagne and we wander around picking up objects and putting them down. I get colder and colder until my whole body is aching. Just outside the Marché des Enfants-Rouges, I stop in my tracks. I have actually frozen.

There's a moment of silence as Adrien registers that I've ceased to exist. Somehow I manage to squeak through Tinman lips, '*Vin. Chaud,*' and he ushers me into a café and orders an emergency hot wine. As I slowly come back to life it dawns on me that this winter business is not to be laughed at. To highlight my stupidity, my glacial cheeks, as they defrost in the warmth, turn a deep beetroot red. I am ashamed. I want to live.

Later that day, tipsy from too much hot wine, Adrien takes me to a pragmatic store and helps me buy the ugliest pret-a-porter quilt I have ever seen, with ugly belt to match. Life with padding feels very different. The feeling of being cold had become like a friend, constantly reminding me of my mortality and, conversely, my aliveness. Now I am warm, safe.

It's dark when we kiss goodbye at the Rambuteau métro steps. I dig my mittens deep into my warm jacket and marvel at how good it feels. Now I will be confident to go out more. And the colder it is, the prettier Paris is – the crisp edges of the buildings and naked trees, the sky the palest turquoise.

The Métro is not a Train

He said to take the train, but what's the difference? I've transcribed his instructions on an old baguette bag and written *train* lots of times in big letters, but as far as I can see, the métro *is* a train and it will be far quicker to take it to the Place de Clichy, then change to line 14 for Asnières.

I launch myself down the métro steps three at a time, feeling a great surge of gratitude for my functioning legs. How do people in wheelchairs survive this city? Come to think of it, I've never seen any disabled people in Paris. Poor and decrepit people, yes, but crutches and walking canes, no.

A train is pulling out as I arrive on the platform and I try to jump on it but the doors slam on my hand and I have to wiggle it back out. Ow. A man in the carriage laughs at me and I flip the bird beneath his window, smiling at him as the train pulls out. She Who Smiles Last Wins. This is my new MO, to be added to my list of Paris rules to live by, along with The Lady in the Boulangerie is Not Your Friend, and Presentation is Everything.

Three whole minutes to wait for the next train. The snack machine is advertising a new Mars Bar. I put in a euro. The Mars Bar sits silent and still in its holster, laughing at my naïveté. I give it the bird inside my pocket and smile furiously.

A black rat runs across the tracks. I wonder if it was black to begin with or is white beneath the soot. A man in a dark trench coat comes to stand next to the snack machine, putting his briefcase down with a sigh. Corporate Prince. He sees me looking and moves away down the platform. I wonder whether the Prince ever saw me looking at him those years ago. Perhaps he had all kinds of fantasies about me too. Perhaps he still does. *Come on, train.*

It crawls to the platform at last and reluctantly opens its doors. I sit facing a beautiful elderly lady in a brown fur jacket, violet stockings, and just enough makeup to accentuate eyes overflowing with the excitement of life. She looks at me like she has a secret to tell. I receive the secret and put it inside myself. We hold eye contact way longer than is customary, then she gets off at Pigalle. The stations rattle by, Montmartre tourists get on and off, a Middle Eastern busker sings 'Isn't She Lovely' to a backing track playing from a little amp on wheels.

At Asnières station I walk up the stairs and out to a large concrete wasteland. Buses pull in and out of a huge bay in front of a smoggy highway with trucks roaring past. It's the most remote space I've seen in Paris. I can't see any of the landmarks Adrien mentioned – the supermarket or the cinema or the café. A lady is pacing back and forth screaming blue murder at a man on a bench. But there is no man on the bench.

Adrien sounds slightly annoyed when I call, though he laughs. 'I said *train*, not métro, from *Saint-Lazare*! About ten times!'

'Oh no, I'm so sorry. I thought it would be quicker from the Place de Clichy.'

Ten minutes later a small blue car comes flying into the bus terminal and pulls up beside me. Adrien looks flustered in a racing driver sort of way. I apologise again and give him a kiss on the cheek and he smiles a little tightly and pulls out. I try not to bounce up and down on the seat. Here I am inside his life, inside his car, inside his normal him. His thick, veiny hand shifts the gearstick in concentrated fury – he's a wild driver but I feel safe. He screeches to a holt at a set of lights and puts his hand on my leg, turning to smile at me. He leans across and kisses me.

Then the lights change and he screams off, negotiating intersections and bends around the village, tailgating and honking.

'Sorry,' he says in English, before breaking back into French as fast as his driving. 'It's just my mother breaks my balls when I borrow the car. That's why I said to take the train, it arrives right near my house.'

'I'm *really* sorry,' I say again. So it's not his car. He tells me he lives just down the road from his mother: a coincidence, he assures me.

I look out the window to see where I am. The streets are wider here, the buildings lower and cleaner. The apartment blocks are bigger and there are even stone houses and walls with trees peering over them, and creepers and flower gardens. Lots of flowerboxes in windows, more than in Paris itself. It's so different and yet just over the *périphérique*.

We come to a lovely street with an old château on it and turn down a stone driveway. He hits the brake, propelling me forward, and says, 'You can get out here.' Then he whips the car into a tiny carport, squeezing himself out to meet me in the driveway.

'This is where my mother lives,' he says, running a hand through his hair. 'Want to meet her?' There is apprehension in his voice.

'I'd love to,' I say, shifting in my shoes.

Séverine lives on the first floor of a quaint old apartment building with white wooden shutters and a flower garden. It feels more like a country manor than a surburban block. The elderly *gardienne* swings open the downstairs door and pinches Adrien's cheeks, saying lots of cute words like *titi* and *mimi*. She bows at me and says, '*Bienvenue mademoiselle.*'

'Madame Debreuil has known me since I was a baby,' Adrien explains as we climb up to the first floor. 'My grandmother lived here before my mother.'

The door to his mother's apartment is half open. We creak through the hallway towards the back of a black bobbed head. The head turns to reveal a striking face with a cigarette dangling from the mouth. She looks like a character from the jazz era. Her face is angular, almost masculine, with no trace of makeup, her expression dry but not humourless. Her teeth have the same brilliant gap as Adrien's.

'*Bonjour*,' she says, stubbing out her cigarette as she stands up. 'Séverine.' We kiss on both cheeks.

'Jayne,' I say. My introduction feels abrupt for the circumstances but I'm not sure what other words to say.

'Hello *toi*,' she says to Adrien, giving him a loaded look.

'Thanks for the car,' he says abruptly, dropping the keys on the table.

'*Oui, merci Séverine*,' I say, apologising clunkily for taking the métro instead of the train. 'I didn't realise there were two stations.'

Séverine waves my apology away, smiling. 'Sit down,' she says, gesturing to a sofa, and these are the last two words I understand as the conversation takes off at the speed of light. She and Adrien occasionally glance towards me and I squawk a *oui* or shrug or smile stupidly, but I'm way out of my depth. I sip the delicious white wine she pours and smoke so hard I get a headspin.

'I do not speeking Inglish,' she says at one point, with an exaggerated frown.

'*Ça va*,' says Adrien, 'Jayne *parle français*.'

Perhaps, but not this fast. All I know is they're having an argument. Feigning understanding, I use my peripheral vision to take in the tasteful apartment, with its rustic floorboards and high old windows. We are sitting in the salon, which adjoins a dining room full of plastic mannequins and torsos and heads on poles, with tape measures and exotic fabrics in all sorts of colours and textures draped over them. A modern sewing machine sits on an old sewing table on a white lace doily. Film posters and etchings and beautiful paintings adorn all the walls. Fairy lights are draped over the windowsills, and even though it's early afternoon and not quite dark yet they are lit. A slender grey cat leaps up and nestles into my lap, then leaps off.

'Shall we go?' asks Adrien suddenly.

Séverine and I kiss on the cheeks and Adrien whisks me out of there.

'I'm sorry,' he says as we walk down the street. 'My mother is driving me crazy at the moment – she's annoyed at me for a stupid reason.' He stops and turns me to him. 'I'm happy you're here.'

'Me too! I'm impatient to see your place.'

'It's very small and *merdique*,' he says and I guess that means shitty.

We walk down through the village with its larger footpaths and cleaner cars, passing a huge white cinema called the Alcazar. We stop in at a butcher's, where an energetic old man hands Adrien a cooked chicken, calling him by his name and raising his eyebrows towards me. The fruit shops are wider and the boulangerie more nondescript and there are big supermarkets and restaurants.

'It's nice here,' I say, as we head off the main street.

'It's okay,' says Adrien.

It's an eight-minute *train* ride from Asnières to Saint-Lazare, right in the middle of Paris. I can see why people live here. It seems easier; fewer people, more space. But I find myself already missing the intensity of the 10th. Here the architecture, the elements, are all similar to *dans* Paris, but it feels a lot more sane.

His apartment is in a pleasant street just off the main thoroughfare. The buildings are more modern, and Adrien's is a tall, flat building with balconies and automatic glass doors downstairs. The lift is clean but smells like cat food and has a big mirror in it. The picture we make is all contrasts. The near-black of his hair and eyes, the blond and blue of mine. His white shirt and black jeans, my red dress and brown boots.

His place is far from the boyish den I'd imagined: a small, neat studio with a tiny kitchen and a real-sized bathroom and balcony, all immaculate and smelling of lavender. Books are lined up alphabetically on shelves, he even has house plants and candles. There's a black-and-white photo of him as a baby, asleep on his mother's naked belly. I move around, picking up objects and turning them over in my fingers, discovering his world. On the bookshelf is a beautiful box with gold embossing that I want to open, but it looks private. Further along the shelf I find a red stamp that reads *Adrien* and stamp it all the way up my arm.

'It's lovely here,' I say, sitting down on his comfortable red sofa, which must double as his bed.

'Thanks.' He goes out onto the balcony and I follow him. The air smells sweet with the distant budding of spring. There's a table with a big fold-out chair and lots of plants, and the balcony faces a beautiful old red-brick apartment building alongside an ugly modern grey one. A man in the ugly one is watching TV with a glass of wine.

'Rub this in your fingers,' Adrien says, passing me a leaf. 'It's *verveine*.'

'What's *verveine*?'

'I'm not sure in English. It's a herb.'

The lemony scent is familiar but I can't place it. It takes me back to a corner of our garden at home, where Mum planted herbs and scented flowers. Adrien senses a shift in me and suggests we go back inside where it's warm.

I sit on the sofa, hands between my knees. I want to make small talk but my French seems to have disappeared.

'Shall I make you a tisane?' he asks, putting water on to boil. When he hands me the tea, there's that scent again – he has put the *verveine* in it, with honey. I sip, it's delicious, but my heart feels weird. I suppress the feeling and say, 'This is lovely tea.'

'Tisane,' he says kindly. 'Not tea.' He explains that tea has theine in it, tisane doesn't.

For dinner he makes a simple pasta with fried zucchini and parmesan on top. We drink red wine as we eat and later we open out his red sofa into a yellow bed and take our clothes off. Adrien is right here with me, looking into my eyes, and I want to be inside my own body and with him, but I'm not. I try to focus on his smooth skin, the tiny freckles on his shoulders. His ceiling is white, his sheets are soft, he is trying to find me. But who is he? His eyes are dark like Mum's – it's strange, they look so familiar and yet so foreign. His face is soft, but still turns a powerful red as he dies his little death. I stay alive. He strokes my back as I fall asleep close to him.

In the morning he gets up in his underpants and puts birdseed in little dishes on the balcony, making kissing noises until tiny birds come. The curtains are open, it's a cool, sunny morning with a new kind of light, a golden colour of early spring, and I watch from the bed as the birds hop and flit around. Coming back inside and seeing that I'm awake, he kisses me, then brings me a croissant and a bowl of coffee. My hair spills into it; Adrien pulls it back for me as I dunk, and kisses my forehead. I ask him about the gold box and he takes it down and opens it: inside is a pale white crystal. I put it against my cheek, then my forehead. It feels cool.

'You talked in your sleep,' he says.

'Really? What did I say?'

'You said – I wrote it down – "There is no 'no'." What does this mean?'

'I have no idea.'

'Then you whispered, "Whatever you do, don't tell anyone."'

'Did I have my eyes open?'

'No.'

'I sometimes sleep with my eyes open. It used to scare my parents.'

He kisses my face gently. 'Do you want to go to Saint-Cloud?'

Yes, I say, without realising what he's talking about. Sun Cloo? Séverine doesn't mind us taking the car this time: it's Sunday and she's sewing.

Saint-Cloud is a posh suburb with a steep park with lush, manicured grass. Adrien holds my hand and we walk beneath tall trees to a hill that looks out over Paris, sit in the sunshine and talk about our friends. I tell him about Marie-France's grace at school and how she cooked me dinner in her gorgeous little Bastille apartment, and showed me her favourite Marcel Marceau and Charlie Chaplin videos. Adrien has a group of friends he wants me to meet.

At lunchtime we drive back to Asnières and he takes me to where the train leaves, the proper train. We share a croque-monsieur at a little bistro below the station.

On the platform, he kisses me intensely as the train pulls in. I feel a mess of excitement and profound disorientation. The doors open and I step into the carriage, where a guy in torn jeans is shouting at a drawn-looking woman covered in piercings. I lean back out and kiss Adrien until the doors beep and the guy jumps off. The pierced woman scowls at me all the way back to Saint-Lazare.

Friday

.

Though it's been a tradition since the '70s for Lecoq students and teachers to frequent Chez Jeannette, the Albanians from the Mauri7 bar across the road, with its Madonna posters, Mucha frescoes, and sticky tables with heavy-set men huddled over them, tempt us across the street with their cheap drinks and cool attitude about us eating our student lunches at their tables. *Qui a bu, boira* reads a plaque behind the bar – 'Who has drunk, will drink' – and we do, on Friday afternoons that spill into Saturday mornings, and on many other nights of the week. But on Friday nights the students from Gaulier, another physical acting school in the suburbs of Paris, come to party with the Lecoq students. Tim, the manager of Mauri7, lets us play our own music and generally own the place, to the bewilderment of the regulars.

I invite Kiki and Adrien to come one Friday night when the bar is particularly steamy and jam-packed with students from both schools. Meg introduces me to a friend of hers from Gaulier, a petite Australian with bright white teeth and a perfect blond bun who I've seen on television back home. Her name is Nadine and she's also on a scholarship. Nadine is with her friend Harry, a documentary film-maker born in Australia and raised in Paris, who with his sand-coloured hair and relaxed clothes looks like he's just emerged from the surf. They both live in the area: Nadine in the 9th and Harry around the corner from me in the rue de Marseille. Neither has heard of the Récollets, and don't know it even when I describe it to them.

Kiki wades through the seething mass of bodies to join us, and I direct everyone down the back, to where Adrien sits sandwiched between a group of Lecoq actors and a couple engaged in a passionate kiss. His back is very straight. He smiles and stands as we approach and I introduce Nadine and Harry. They all kiss and Nadine is pulled away by a friend, leaving Adrien, Kiki, Harry and me standing in an uncomfortably close formation until the kissing couple conveniently leave and we have room to sit down.

'It's my birthday!' Kiki says to Adrien with glee, holding up the bracelet I bought her.

'Ow hold are you?' asks Adrien politely.

'Old!' she says and jumps up to grab a waiter, leaving me sitting between Harry and Adrien on the banquette, unable to talk to both at once. I hold Adrien's hand as I talk to Harry about the recent Australian election, trying to communicate at the same time with Adrien with my back. After a while I make an excuse to go to the bathroom, so as to change the formation, and when I return Adrien and Harry are talking in French. Relieved, I go to find Kiki. She's in the corner talking to Marc Finland.

A waitress comes over with a tray of shots.

'Down the hatch!' says Kiki, and we throw back the spicy vodka, which makes me prickle all over.

A tap on my shoulder. Marie-France. I hug her and introduce her to Kiki, handing her a shot. She looks at it like she doesn't know what to do with it.

'Drink it!' I say.

She puts her velvety lips to the glass and takes a tiny sip.

'*Oui*,' she says. 'It's good.'

'You *tasted* it?'

She doesn't understand what I mean and hands the shot back to me. Kiki lifts it from my grip and slams it down, turning back to Marc.

'Come and meet my boyfriend,' I say, leading Marie-France away.

Adrien is still talking to Harry on the banquette. 'This is Marie-France,' I say. 'The one who is good at everything.' They kiss on the cheeks and start chatting in French. With her beautiful black dress and silky hair, she and Adrien look like the perfect Parisian couple. His shoulders relax as soon as they begin to chat and an uncomfortable feeling passes through my body: shouldn't he be with someone like her? I brush it off. The vodka has hit and my spirits are only lifting.

Harry gets up and we join Kiki and Marc, who have begun to dance, and we jiggle and jump around with them. I am quite drunk. Kiki is dancing like a maniac. Marie-France comes to join us and starts moving like a cat, the animal she had chosen this week for *autocours* (and got slammed by the teachers). I flap my wings and gyrate my neck like my equally failed chicken. The music gets louder and Tim keeps giving everyone free shots, turning all the Lecoq students into animals, jumping and gyrating and slinking around like a freak circus. The Gaulier students do the same. If an alien walked in they would categorise us as some kind of horny, stinky, half-human, half-animal tribe. I'm swept up in it and then Adrien is with me and I tone it down a bit to meet his gentler pace. I'm dripping in my skimpy dress and his face is flushed in his heavy cream knit.

'Take it off!' I yell, tugging at it.

He yanks it down. 'No, no.'

'You'll die!' I can see he has a T-shirt on underneath and I tug again.

'No, I can't,' he says, looking uncomfortable. 'I would feel naked.'

The music changes. Kiki is dancing like a wildcat. 'Adrien!' she yells. 'What animal do you do?'

'A human!'

There is a strange energy between the two of them, but I'm not sure what it is. All is blurred by booze.

We dance until my mouth is dry, and Adrien squeezes my hand. '*On y va?*' he asks, and we kiss everyone goodbye and leave.

Out in the crisp night air I lean on him and we stumble side by side up the Faubourg-Saint-Denis to my room, where I fall on the floor and splay out my legs and arms. Adrien goes to make a tisane.

'No, come here,' I call, floppy arms flailing. 'Come here.'

He puts the saucepan on and comes to kneel awkwardly on the floor, allowing me to fling my arms around his neck. I plunge my face into him, drinking in his perfume.

'You smell nice,' I slur. 'I've never known a man-perfume that smells nice before.'

'Oh, you are so drunk,' he says, half laughing.

'I'm *not*,' I say, putting my face on the seat of the red chair. 'I am not drunk.' I turn and smile at him. 'What's drunk in French?'

He passes me a cup of tea and sits on the chair. '*Bourrée*,' he says. 'And you are – you are *bourrée, tu t'es bourré la gueule!*'

I'm drunk off my face, in other words. They use the word 'face' a lot for things. 'To do the face' is to be angry. 'Your face!' means shut up.

I gulp my tea and scald my mouth, squealing, then push my fingers into the fold of skin that has come loose on my upper palate. He looks at me with a pretend look of reprehension and I look back like a naughty child.

'Kiki, she is *lesbienne, non?*'

'What?' I laugh. 'Kiki is the reddest-blooded heterosexual I know. Are you serious?'

'Well, she is *bi, alors.*'

'Oh my god,' I say. 'Where did you get that idea?'

'I see Kiki with the girls. And Martine, her friend from the party where we meet, she is *bi*. So, I just thinking …'

'Did you think I was a lesbian then too, at the party? You're so funny!' I giggle, rolling onto my stomach. 'Hey, loosen up! Look at you, sitting there on my throne. Come down here with me, you big, gay-scared —'

'Hmm,' he says, dropping to his knees.

'Was one of your exes gay or something?'

'*Non.*'

'Well, I can assure you that I am very heterosexual. I even kissed a girl once to find out.'

This wasn't the right thing to say.

'Oh, man,' I say. 'I just wanted to experience everything. But when it came down to it, I wasn't interested. I was doing it to be cool, and to tick it off. Didn't you have your obligatory gay experience? At your fancy boys' college?'

He looks shocked. '*Non.*'

'Okay then, fine. Can we just agree that we're not gay? And be together?'

He smiles. 'Okay. We're not gay.'

'And can we just speak French? We're so formal in English. I can speak your language better now – let's do that?'

'*D'accord.*'

Mayday

It seems Harry and I have the same trajectories around the 10th and I bump into him four times in the following week: in the boulangerie, by the canal, on my way to school, and in the supermarket. After that one I invite him up for a beer and to show him the Récollets, and he can't believe how many times he must have walked past it and not seen it.

Nadine is the same. For some reason, the majestic old white building just seems to miss your eye if you're not looking for it. I notice this phenomenon with a lot of people I mention it to. Perhaps it's a portal.

She invites me over one morning, to recover after a night out with Harry and Kiki at the hip bar-gallery the Point Éphémère. Adrien was invited, but for some reason he hadn't shown. When I called, he simply said he wasn't coming, without feeling the need to offer an excuse.

Nadine shares a luxurious top-floor apartment with two wealthy French people, and I'm sitting on her sunlit balcony drinking coffee when Adrien rings.

'Yes?' I say.

'*Ma chérie*,' he says, sensing my attitude. 'Are you doing the face?'

'Yes,' I say.

'What are you doing today?' he asks, ignoring my tone. He tells me his friend Fabien is back from the Maldives, where he runs a fancy resort, and they're going to drive to another friend's château in the country.

Nadine has a lunch date, the sun is shining, and I can't think of anything I'd rather do than drive out to the country. I've been dreaming for a long time of French countryside, the grass, fresh air.

'Maybe,' I say.

'Come, *ma chérie*, you'll like it.'

I give it a few more seconds before agreeing.

'Come now, because Fab will be here in half an hour.'

Nadine smiles at me as I hang up. 'Nice try.'

'Jesus, look what I'm wearing,' I say, looking at her. All that was clean this morning was a vintage floral pinafore, a worn black tunic and high red socks, which I paired with my over-the-knee brown suede boots. Raggedy Ann chic. I was hungover and running late for Nadine's. I hadn't even showered.

'You look great,' she says, admiring my stupid outfit. I rush out the door before I'm tempted to start ransacking her wardrobe, which is much more appropriate but two sizes too small for me.

It's hot on the train and a man plays a trumpet loudly in my ear. I give him two euros to shut up but it just encourages him. The sun lights up the Seine as we cross, the trumpet man gets off, and by the time I reach Adrien's I've forgiven him. He kisses me passionately and gives me a hug that lifts me off the ground.

'*T'es jolie!*' he says, standing back to look at me.

'I wasn't expecting a date,' I say, clutching at myself.

A well-groomed guy exits the bathroom.

'Jayne,' says Adrien, 'Fabien.'

'*Bonjour,*' says Fabien, kissing me rhythmically on both cheeks. He is dapper – dark hair slicked back and a mauve polo shirt with the collar pulled up.

Fab has a cool car, cool hair, and speaks with a cool aristo-drawl. He and Adrien went to boarding school together – one of the best schools in France, Adrien has told me – along with Raphaël and Nico, whose family owns the château we're going to. Adrien was a poor boy amongst the richest boys in France – not that he was actually poor, he just wasn't from a family *de nom*. He doesn't have a *de* in his surname, or a champagne named after him, or famous paintings that have been handed down through his family for centuries. I'm not sure Fab comes from one of those families, but judging from his loftiness he seems to. Though he gesticulates a lot, and that, according to what we've been learning at school, makes you lower status. The higher the status, the slower the movement and the less frequent the speech. At the highest status, people barely move or speak at all. While Fab moves his arms around, it's in a very fluid and confident way. He speaks down to Adrien, booming over him. I don't exist. Instead of fighting it I let myself disappear, along with Paris, as the city opens out into the suburbs, then towns and then lush green meadows. It's the first time I've left the Paris region and I'm glued to my window, oblivious to the conversation in the front seat.

When we reach a rolling part of the countryside, Fab pulls the top down and I can no longer hear their conversation at all. The wind whips at my ears and the earthy smell of fresh-cut grass and cow shit fills my nose between blasts of smoke from Fab's joint. We drive and drive, past fields and through little glades and tiny stone towns where, if I block out the parked cars and advertising, I can imagine it's the year 1700. We pass a big zoo and Fab and Adrien point at it and laugh. Adrien turns around and tells me a story about it but I can't hear so I just nod and smile. He passes me the joint. Fab closes the roof and asks me about Australia and why I am in Paris and I try to explain, but it's too complicated and he can't hear me anyway so we all just give up and go back to what we were doing.

On the outskirts of a village, Fab pulls off the road where an elderly couple are selling little posies of white flowers on a card table. They smell divine – lily-of-the-valley, or *muguet*, as Adrien tells me. The couple are poor and humble and kind. Fab buys the two loveliest posies on the table and the sweet-faced couple put a bit of crêpe paper around them, wrap a ribbon around the paper and tie it in a bow. Fab flings the posies in the back seat as we tear off, leaving the couple in a cloud of dust.

After an hour's drive we pull into a stone driveway and Fab yells something into an intercom in front of two enormous gates. They creak open and we drive slowly along a vast field with a château in the distance that has all the chimneys and turrets and statues and shutters of fairytales. My mouth is agape as we approach and veer off towards the right, beneath a forest of trees. Adrien tells me the building is usually open to the public, but today it's closed for the holiday. Nico's family live in an elegant, hedged-in house beside the château. We emerge from the trees at the open front door and walk through the opulent yet homely rooms to the kitchen, where we can see people milling outside. I put the flowers in glasses of water on the marble kitchen table, not in a hurry for the introductions.

Adrien grabs my hand and we step through a doorway onto a vast stone terrace with an outdoor table under luxurious umbrellas. Beyond is a vast manicured lawn with a tennis court, farmland in the distance. A parade of young women and men file one by one past us. Eight girls and seven boys kiss me on both cheeks and say, 'Sabine,' 'Agathe,' 'Thérèse,' and so on, to which I reply, 'Jayne, Jayne, Jayne, Jayne.' Adrien has told me that on such occasions you don't have to engage with each person and say something like 'Nice to meet you.' It only slows the process down and is insincere. 'You don't know them yet,' he said. 'How can you be sure it's nice to meet them?'

At the end of the line, a guy who knows my name says, 'Salut Jayne,' and I reply, 'Jayne.' When I realise what I've done I let out a loud, ugly laugh. He doesn't laugh and neither does anyone else.

Each one of them is wearing a variation of French tennis attire: pastel polo shirts, crisp white shorts, neat day dresses, visors. Not only do they all know each other and speak the same language fast and fluently, they have all been to Ralph Lauren together to buy their outfits. I must look like an alien.

Adrien doesn't mind my uniqueness; on the contrary, he seems to step up his public affection for me, playing with the straps on my dress, draping his arm across my shoulder, kissing me lightly and squeezing my hand, trying to involve me in conversations. I feel we are being watched and judged and Adrien looks like he's enjoying this. I have the sense that his friends are not. They probably all attended balls together; perhaps Adrien lost his virginity to one of these girls, surely at least one is in love with him. There's a tightness between them all, a sense of ownership, like an incestuous royal family.

The boys go off to kick a football and I join the girls under the umbrella as they nibble thinly sliced charcuterie and sip glasses of rosé. They are so high-status their faces barely move when they speak, which is softly, in graceful sounds; they sit and smoke and drawl and never, ever laugh loudly or guffaw or tell bad jokes or burp. None of them wear makeup, yet their skin is translucent-smooth; there's no brazen lipstick or big dob of concealer on a crusted zit. Their hair is neat, it has never once been dyed pink; their skin shows no sign of teenage piercings or bad tattoos. They ask me about Australia and have no interest in my reply. I ask them about Paris and they have no interest in their reply. I am an annoyance to them, a glitch in their seamless party; they just want to catch up on their lives in their silken language, and here is this girl in a floral pinafore raping their language with a hacksaw.

So this is what it is to be the foreigner, I think to myself. The outsider. I try to imagine Adrien around the barbecue at home and I can't.

I stay until it feels physically painful for us all, then go off to join the boys. They're on a patch of lawn beneath the trees, rolling and ducking and tackling each other like lion cubs. I run in and try to steal the ball. It occurs to me that the game has become awkward and I realise the boys are embarrassed that I'm playing with them. All except Adrien, who passes the ball to me, flushed and smiling. The girls watch from under their umbrella, faces bemused.

I leave the game and flop on the grass under a tree, rolling my stupid socks down and crossing my arms behind my head. Birds chirp. Cows moo in the distance. The grass smells delectable; I breathe it in. Adrien comes and flops next to me, panting. He turns onto his side and begins caressing my hair. I smile beneath my hand-visor, keeping my eyes firmly shut. It's better here, where I can imagine I'm inside the world. He kisses me on the lips and pulls me gently to my feet, leading me behind the trunk and kissing me sweetly again. Fab whistles at us on his way to the terrace and we pull apart.

'Want to see my cartwheel?' I ask Adrien, and when he nods I hurl myself across the grass. Then I stand in a strong handstand, my back and shoulder muscles firm from acrobatics training at school. He comes and puts his hand on my lower back and I ease my weight across his hand and flip over to standing.

'Watch,' he says, and moving a long way back, takes a run-up and performs a perfect flip, landing on his feet.

'I didn't know you could do a *saut de mains*!'

'*Mais oui*,' he says, 'I'm a pro!'

I get him to stay where he is and I walk back, run up, and spring off my hands, near where he's standing. He puts his hand in the same place on my lower back and I flip right over.

'I barely touched you then!' he says. '*Tiens, regarde.*' He grabs my hands and pushes them down to the grass, showing me how to get more spring out of them. I run back and try to do the flip on my own but land abruptly on my butt. I laugh like a four-year-old before running back to try again. And again. I can't quite pull it off.

'We will keep practising,' says Adrien, smiling, flushed.

I don't care that they're all watching, smoking on the terrace. I don't care that Mum is thinking, Will you *ever* grow up? I don't care about anything right now. I can almost do an unassisted *saut de mains*. Thanks to Adrien.

'*À table!*' call the girls.

Adrien leapfrogs over me as I go to stand up. I leap back over him and we leapfrog all the way to the table.

Thérèse serves him a golden chicken wing and Adrien and I continue our ridiculous conversation about how leapfrogging in French is called leap-sheeping. Perhaps, I say, it's because of counting sheep leaping over a fence in order to sleep. I say that I think the French version is more poetic, and keep babbling as they eat with their heavy silver cutlery. Smothered giggles flutter around the table and I'm not sure if they're laughing at my attempted humour or at me.

'Who wants rosé?' someone asks. Once the delicious chicken, or *pintade*, is finished we squash tiny portions of mouth-watering cheeses onto our plates with salad, and then eat berries with cream. A wooden pergola with a pretty roped creeper creates a dappled light over us. Cigarettes are lit, glasses refilled, and a pleasant afternoon drunkenness sets itself into my body.

Nico comes and drapes himself over the arm of Adrien's seat and smiles at the sky, exhaling plumes of smoke at it. He looks like someone from *The Great Gatsby*. His polo shirt is pale mauve, like Fabien's, and he's wearing khaki pants and a beautiful white Panama hat. He holds his cigarette in a camp way and I think he's gay, but then many of Adrien's straight friends give that impression.

'I have never seen a girl kick a football quite like you,' Nico says to me, and Adrien laughs.

'She's Australian,' he says.

'Yes, a real Australian,' agrees Nico, as if he knows what that is. I feel objectified, like a curiosity, but I smile anyway, through my sun-drenched rosé haze. I suppose I see them as objects too, pretty snowdomes to shake up and admire. Especially Adrien, with his Ken-doll face looking across the table at me as he smokes his cigarette. Did I ever think he would actually be real? That night I first met him he was like some kind of French mirage, a man I'd invented who then appeared in the flesh, but did I really imagine going deeper inside him, as I am now? Had he imagined that with me?

'Shall we take a little promenade?' asks Nico. The others are leaving the table for the pool, the tennis court, the kitchen, the lawn.

Adrien helps me through a secret garden gate and we crunch our way along a stone path to the château grounds. He knows this place well, he tells me; he used to stay with Nico's family on school holidays when Séverine was away working. Nico and he laugh about something and I walk behind them, tuning out. The white linen of Adrien's shirt billows behind him in the breeze. Nico has sweat gathering in beads on the skin of his tanned neck. The fragrant smoke of their *pétard* blows back in my face. We pass perfect hedges and little ponds with bright red fish swimming in them and a beautiful statue of a woman's face covered in deep green moss, which Nico tells me is one of his ancestors.

I am sweating in my socks and the sun is beating down sharply, and in the heat and the beauty I feel a rising horniness. We keep walking, past fountains and through a mini forest, over a rippling stream and into a little glen, the boys murmuring, the sun beating, the birds chirping. My mind wanders across all kinds of situations, sinking into the stream with them both, naked in the glen, rolling in leaves, being discovered by the girls, who, shocked at first, take off their visors and join us …

As we exit a glade, Adrien reaches behind and touches my hand, as if he has heard my thoughts. Maybe he can feel my heat. I rub my closed hand around inside his fingers in a dirty way; I want to steal him away, devour his body. He is randy too, I can feel it in the tips of his fingers, the way they curl to receive my finger-job.

In the château the rooms are decked in red carpet and have windows so high the floors are bathed in light. The beauty and history makes me dizzy. I can't help but imagine the people in here over centuries, having sex, giving birth, dying. Nico gives us the tour and we tag along like first-home buyers, Adrien's hands behind his back, my hand in his. The bedroom walls are covered in the same material as the curtains and there are chandeliers and bedposts in the shape of ducks. The restraint is making me crazy. As Nico leads us through a dark cellar in single file, I reach my arms around and grab Adrien's nipples, kiss his neck. He gropes at my thighs. If I had a cock I would push it right into him.

In an old galley kitchen full of old stoves and ovens and murderous ghosts, Nico turns to us and we pull apart. 'And here's where all the food was made. So *voilà*! Your private tour ends here.'

'It's very impressive,' I say.

'I have never seen it empty like this,' says Adrien, running his hands along the pots and pans strung up on hooks, making them crash loudly.

All I see on the way back to the manor are sex spots; ferny dens, thick tree trunks and even a hedge maze, but I can't get Adrien away from Nico and his friends, so my heat goes slowly cold with the disappearing sun, leaving me with gritted teeth. I spend the remainder of the day alone in the shadows, feeling awkward and vulnerable. By the time evening has set in and we get into Fab's car, I'm in a dark mood.

'What a magnificent day,' says Fab as he pulls out.

Adrien agrees, wiggling his hand behind his seat and into mine.

'And for you, Jayne?' asks Fab.

I tell him it was okay and when he presses I relent and say I found it hard to fit in.

Fab laughs. 'These are probably not your sort of people.'

He may not have meant that in a rude way – perhaps he doesn't see himself as one of them either. Regardless, I feel the urge to tear up his pristine back seat with my fingernails.

I squeeze Adrien's hand hard and he turns around.

'Sorry, *chérie*. They are particular.'

I stare out the window the whole way home. A house is on fire somewhere, trucks race. Adrien's hair flicks above his headrest. I feel the urge to pull it but then he peeks between the gap with a complicit smile: somehow we are in this together.

Back in Asnières we wave Fab off and I am glad he lives in the Maldives. Adrien and I stand in an awkward silence in the lift. In the apartment he opens the blinds and we go out onto the balcony where the air is still warm. He fills a watering can and waters his plants as I watch the man in the building opposite watch his TV, slumped in his chair.

'Sorry, *ma chérie*. I didn't realise everyone would be there.'

I try to explain how I felt. He must have felt strange too, surely.

'No,' he laughs, putting the watering can back in its place. 'Yes.' He turns to me with a soft look on his face. 'But that's not because of you. They're very old friends, old families, they are very … shut.'

'You say "they", but you're one of them.'

'No, I'm not.'

He's always been on the outside, he says. Artistic at school, in the theatre club, the only one not in line to take over the family business, inherit the fortune. An only child, fatherless, with a mother who was a costume designer in cinema.

'They keep me around as their toy. And they liked my old girlfriend, so they were being cold with me today.'

'She was French?'

'Yes.'

'Why didn't you stay with her?'

'Because *I* didn't like her. I want you! I love how you are, you're so weird. It was so funny when you talked about the leap-sheeping.'

His arms wind their way around my waist. I like that he likes me weird. But being on the outer is not fun. I bury my face in his neck.

My initiation to Adrien's friends was, to say the least, shaky. But in the following weeks he involves me in more social events and things begin to thaw. One Saturday he invites me to dinner at a fancy restaurant on top of the Samaritaine building with the group from the château. The restaurant is called Kong and they all pronounce it Kon-g, and the chairs are made of see-through plastic with the faces of supermodels on the backs. I'm a little more at ease in my Nadine-approved black dress, and even when I complain to the waiter in Paul's three-year-old voice that my fish is *dégueulasse*, nobody minds; in fact the table agrees that the food is shit and they wish they had the guts to use a word like that to describe their own meals. Though I still feel like a curiosity, I'm getting beyond the surface of these people, who are all looser beneath their taut exteriors.

On the way back to Adrien's in the car, Raphaël sings along to an English pop song on the radio, mimicking the language with a whole lot of made-up words and exaggerated vowel sounds. Apparently this is called 'yoghurt', and Adrien does it all the time when I play him a song, or when he wants to take the piss of out something I'm saying. Raphaël's girlfriend, Thérèse, who is driving, turns the music off and he goes on singing his own made-up song, something about a spanking, enjoying making us laugh.

Raphaël commutes to London a lot with his work, so his English is mildly better than the others'. 'Oooh, spank me, baybeee, get that spankee vibe,' he sings. The more it tickles me, the more it eggs him on, until tears are falling down my cheeks.

'You should put that out as a single,' I tell him.

A few days later he invites Adrien and me to dinner, but I have late rehearsals. As it seems like we're becoming friends, I decide to send him a personal message.

'Sorry I can't make it on Friday Raph,' I text. 'But spank you very much for the invite.'

A few days later, Adrien brings it up.

'Raph told me about your message,' he says.

'What message?'

'The spanky message.'

'Oh!' I laugh.

'He was embarrassed about it – he said he thought I should know, and showed me the text.'

'Hang on. He didn't think it was funny?'

'It wasn't funny. You were coming on to him?'

I feel stunned. Of all people, I thought Raphaël would be able to take a joke. I sigh, and put my head in my hands. 'I don't know how to be!'

There is a line somewhere that I keep tripping over. Landmines everywhere.

In a bar in Saint-Germain-des-Prés one night, I manage to offend Nico too. He and Adrien are going away the next day on a weekend hike, and, overestimating my easygoing friendship with Nico, I drape my arm around him and tell him that I won't mind if he and Adrien need to cuddle up at night together in the tent, to keep each other warm. It is such a cute and innocent image, I think it will make him laugh, but he goes red in the face, and so does Adrien, which, instead of making me shut up, only makes me drive the joke harder. My sister would be rolling her eyes. *Let it go, idiot.* But I'm circling the bar, quizzing the French population on whether they think it's funny or not. Most look at me as though I'm insane.

After almost falling off my bike riding too fast across the river, I get home to a message from Nico: *Just for you know, I like Adrien as friends, friends only.*

Aargh!

I don't understand why it's not obvious to them that I know Nico wouldn't be having an affair with Adrien, or that I wouldn't so brazenly start something with Raphaël. It's only funny to me because it seems so ludicrous.

They both accept my apology, and Adrien laughs. 'You're crazy. But I like you.'

To like something is to *aime* it. Like an apple. But to love someone is to *aime* them too. When he says he likes me he says, '*Je t'aime beaucoup*.' Which means 'I like you a lot.' You have to add a word at the end to dilute it.

I tell him I love him at Le Sporting, the restaurant down by the canal with the black-and-white photos of boxers on the walls and the weird name. Then I lean across the table and look into his eyes.

It feels good to speak the words. Saying them in French provokes a different sensation than in my own language: there is flair and colour and danger in the foreign words, and also a touch of Godard film intrigue. I have been curious to know if they might break me from this sensation of living in a dream. They don't, but hearing him say the words back creates a massive spark.

He leans over the table to give me a long, sultry kiss as the waitress looks on, revolted.

Twenty Movements

A major part of our end-of-year assessment is the famous *vingt mouvements*. Individually, in front of the entire school, we must perform our own sequence – or *enchaînement* – of Jacques Lecoq's twenty mime and acrobatics moves, which we've been learning to master since the first day of school. It's the first time in the year we will choreograph and perform something on our own. It is said that no two *enchaînements* have ever been the same.

I am extremely proud of mine: it has a flowing logic that moves each gesture gracefully to the next, from the cartwheel to the harlequin, from the handstand to undulation. I have practised and practised in the cellar at the Récollets, the spirits of the monks urging me on.

It's my turn. I take my place in the centre of the *Grande Salle*, breathe. I feel nervous but strong; my body has developed new muscles that ignore my nerves and do their own thing. The students and teachers, seated, are dead silent.

I begin with the *éclosion*, moving from the tightest ball and opening out as far into a star shape as my body will reach, then I ease fluently into the cartwheels, and on goes my fluid *enchaînement*. My handstand is perfect: I hold it for several seconds before falling down into the warrior pose and undulating. As I move into 'climbing the wall' I think I hear a sniff and what sounds like a giggle. I push on. Clean, precise. Another giggle. Am I hearing things? I stay focused and end up back in a ball, just as I began. The metamorphosis is complete.

Raucous clapping. I stand in front of the group, proud and shy.

'Bravo, Jayne,' says Claude. He has a strange smile on his face.

Angela is open and warm. 'This was very good,' she says. '*Un bel enchaînement.*'

Boris, I now see, has dewy eyes like he's been laughing, and has his hand over his mouth. 'There is this thing,' he says. 'It's hard to explain.'

'It's her feet,' says Ju-Yong.

'Yes,' says Angela. 'You have this strange thing with your feet. And perhaps your neck – the way your head sits on your neck. It's a very small detail, but quite specific.'

'You don't *mean* to be funny,' says Boris, 'you are so serious. But something about the way your body is put together, the angle of your feet – it doesn't match up with your seriousness. So it comes across as funny.'

My classmates agree by smiling. This appraisal is not, of course, what I want to hear. I want to be taken seriously. They liked my *enchaînement* but my feet are weird? I feel weak at the thought that my weird feet and head may stop me getting through to second year.

The other students' pieces are fascinating. Each movement is technically the same – the cold, precise executions we have all learnt throughout the year. And while there's nothing emotional in a handstand, or miming rowing a boat, somehow, in putting together a piece, the actor's personality comes through so clearly it moves people to tears. It's as though the soul shines through in the gaps between the movements.

Marie-France's sequence is sad in its perfection, each movement beautifully executed, but somehow she feels like a lost ballerina, searching for something. Ravi Canada's is vulnerable in its playfulness. The Spanish Amélie's is hopeful in its messiness.

Afterwards it doesn't seem to matter whether we are accepted into second year or not: we have seen each other. We drink ourselves into a stupor at Mauri7 and sing on the tables into the night.

The next day, everyone is pale as we sit in the foyer waiting to be called in and told our destiny. I have no picture of what I'll do if I don't get into second year. I just see black. I face my fate with the knowledge that I've done all I could. I have bruised and blistered and calloused my body, pummelled my ego, almost broken a finger, been bashed in the head with a broom. I've pushed, relented, made a fool of myself over and over and over again and occasionally got a silent nod or a *bien* and one *pas mal*. I've stayed up all night trying to juggle three balls, got up at four am every day for a week to follow Paris streetcleaners as research for a piece, done two thousand handstands, mastered a solo *saut-de-mains*. I've tried dominating, yielding, going too far and not doing enough. I've worked well with people I don't like and horribly with those I like. I've done my absolute best. If they tell me it's over, I will go into the abyss knowing I had nothing more to give.

Almost all of us want to do second year, but everyone I talk to has a plan B. Marie-France will go back to being an *intermittent du spectacle*, a supported government actor doing regular gigs, or perhaps teach, although it's hard to imagine her not getting in. Umi and Yoshi Japan will go home. Ravi Canada will start his own company.

The faces begin to drift down from the top of the stairs. It's easy to read the results. Anja Sweden is in. Jamie London is in. So is the Spanish Amélie, but she tells me she's returning to Madrid: she has a theatre back home waiting for her and never intended to stay. The other four Spaniards are in. Bethany Scotland isn't, and is in tears in Lara Dublin's arms. Meg London, Faye Ohio and Marie-France are in. Laurent is not in and is furious. Neither of the Greek girls are in, and are ashen.

I want to be in. I want to stay here where the trees change. Where it snows. Where nobody wears helmets or obeys the road rules. Where killing yourself by smoking is a fact of life, where being an intermittent actor is a normal job. Where being alone isn't lonely anymore, where I can just walk and walk and look at things and come home feeling full on life, like I've gorged myself just from looking. Where the language sounds like velvet and water and caramel and honey, and letter-writing is still a normal form of communication. Where chequebooks will never go out of fashion and nor will inkwells and quills and calligraphy artists. Where bookbinders and button-makers and violin-shapers still work away quietly in their shops, where Sundays are still Sundays and the city is calm. Where some days I dress up for the city and not for anybody else, put lipstick on for her, some eyeshadow, my nicest shoes, and just walk in her. Where the completion of a task as menial as buying a stamp and sending a letter feels like a major accomplishment. Where I feel alive, more alive than ever before.

Please, let me stay in Paris. I will be good.

'Jayne?' calls the voice from above. Marie-France squeezes my hand as I head for the stairs and then sit to wait on the same fold-down chair I sat on the day I enrolled. The *Grande Salle* is empty, the wind outside blows leaves against the skylights.

Angela pokes her head out the door and beckons me in.

'Sit down,' she says, and I sit in the big leather chair feeling minuscule.

'Can I speak in French?' she asks and I nod, though I instantly regret it as she launches into a discourse I can't quite follow. She then stops, looks me dead in the eye and says, 'It's a *oui*.'

It's a *oui*!

Be calm, I order myself. Be calm and listen.

'Now you must push … No more time for hesitation … During the year you were like this' – she draws a chart in the air of ups and downs – 'next year there is no time for this. We do not take you by the hand. Next year is something else, it is up to you to push your ideas. We can see you know why you're here. Stop being scholarly. Move more, think less. Don't look for results in order to grow bigger.'

'Okay,' I say.

'Do you have questions?'

'No,' I say, though I have loads, I just can't phrase them quickly enough.

I leave with her words buzzing around my head. I have been trying too hard to impress them, to be a good student. This, it seems, is not a good thing. But I'm in. I'm in! I breathe for a moment before walking down the stairs in front of the gallery of heads looking up, placing on my face a neutral but open look that reads *yes*, but not too much.

⁓

Dad is happy for me, and says he knew I'd get in. He has decided to retire from the television station and buy a small man-house by the beach we went to on holidays as kids. He has found a rock there he likes to sit on. I think about Mum's wardrobe. Her old porcelain Sally doll up there with her painted red nails. Her coats that you fall into. The knits with her smell in them.

Kate tells me I suck and she doesn't want me to come home anyway. Her new housemate actually does the dishes and doesn't require that she hide chocolate. When she told the housemate I was in Paris, the housemate said, 'She's never coming back.'

'I'll be back,' I say. 'Just not this year.'

'Good, we don't have room for you anyway, country's full.'

'Why don't you come here?'

'Because I don't want to.'

She will be okay. The boys are okay. Dad is okay. They are all okay. It's okay.

Adrien comes straight over and, without a word, tugs off my clothes and we bash around the studio, having a huge little death together on my tiny kitchen-table top, then falling asleep on the floor before he gets dressed in a barman's outfit and runs out to a one-off catering gig. I lie all night staring at the moth, in its spot near E.T. With the fear of not making it through gone, and with the prospect of a long break from school, I should feel elated. But for some reason I feel strange. Now that I'm in and can see the year ahead, a flood of new questions arrives.

What are you doing? the moth asks. People are calling you *madame*. And you're throwing yourself around a room being a camembert cheese, an operatic chicken, a drop of water swept out into a raging ocean ...

Dancing around in the city of light, trying to touch it. Paris. The beauty. The grime. The tits-on-end anticipation. The colours and thoughts and songs and sounds and smells and germs and children and dogs. The cardboard beds outside the Gare de l'Est, the taste of strawberries, the sky, last métro, first métro, foamy piles of spit on the pavement, the bells, the dreams, the light in my tree ...

Adrien. His handwriting, the new words and expressions, his blank looks after yet another of my *faux pas*. The grave errors of conjugation. The correctness of things. His hair in the mornings, the taste of his skin, the *mon amours* and the *chérie je t'aimes*, the way his mouth moves when he speaks. The misunderstandings, mistranslations, miscommunications, mistrust, mystery. The mist. The missed. The trying and wanting and asking and wondering and spinning around and around and around ...

I am the moth. The night butterfly. Turning in circles now on E.T.'s face, saying come on, come on, girl, it's time to grow up, time to take control.

I'm living. And I'm changing. I'm a child. And a girl. And a woman. And my grandmother. And not born yet. And dead. This biology. The grass-roots, animal baseness of it all. I'm a root machine like everyone else, just wanting to fuck and grow round and shoot out spawn like the rest of the fishes, to hang my eggs over the precipice, to bury my offspring in a warm ditch. I am the cat from the Festi Bazar, with crumbling ears, pumping out litters and litters in cupboards and corners, just shitting them out, spewing forth reams of seething maggots, vomiting up tiny ratty copies of myself and washing their shitty nappies and sending them to school.

I dream of babies, fat ones, tiny ones, of miniature girls in prams and sons dressed in tutus and babies that speak perfect French and give me very serious information, and babies that are dead and floating in the sea.

One is not born a woman. One becomes a woman. My nature is not calibrating with my brain. It is independent. An alien growth.

Help me, Simone de Beauvoir. Help me know what it all means.

Summer

There are six whole weeks off school. I line up at the mothership to see if they'll keep paying my monthly cash support, and to my astonishment they hand over the envelope. I look around to see if I'm to be handcuffed, then slip out past the security man who says, '*Au revoir mademoiselle.*' It's enough money to almost get by, but certainly not enough to go on holiday with, much as I long to put my feet on sand or green grass, which Adrien reminds me is a summer luxury reserved for the rich, not theatre students and out-of-work actor/models who can't pay their hot-water bill. None of his friends have invited us to their houses in Saint-Tropez or Biarritz, but he says there's always hope.

I can't go away anyway, I have to find a job: the small inheritance Mum left me, which has been supplementing my survival over the past year, is almost gone. Nadine gives me her acting agent's number, but the woman hangs up on me when I tell her I'm still studying. I need to think of something creative, short-term and flexible. I could write stories for the newspapers back home. Or be a DJ, like that girl at Martine's party. Or an English teacher. This seems most logical. I put up a notice at the Récollets and the Cité advertising private English tuition, but Kiki reminds me that most of the residents speak English, and that we're in France. I put up another notice advertising French tuition, saying *Study* *French* *with someone* *nice*, because learning French can be so boring and oppressive. Then I take it down because I don't want to be nice, and also that's offensive to those French people who are also very nice, like Marie-France.

Marie-France appreciates that I've taken it down. She loathes the myth that French people are rude. They're just honest, she says. I agree, but now my marketing angle is shot. Tatiana says she'll give me regular babysitting with Miru when they get back from Japan. That can hold me until something magical happens.

Kiki goes away on a yoga retreat, Nadine goes to her rich housemate's place in Normandy, Harry goes surfing on the Atlantic coast, and Marie-France goes to live at her grandmother's down south for the whole of summer. Adrien is stuck in Paris with me. When we're not mooching around the parks or standing under mist machines on Paris Plage, the sandy 'beach' Mayor Delanoë has installed along the Seine (which Harry likens to the carpark at Bondi Beach, minus the beach), we take cold showers and lie in swimwear on his balcony, smoking hash and imagining we're looking at the Atlantic Ocean rather than the banal brick block across the way. He teaches me more slang and street expressions and how to swear in French, which I practise for tone and attitude. I teach him how to speak Australian, helping him master 'Go and get fucked' (the cornerstone of the dialect and key to mastering the accent, according to Ravi Canada, along with the word 'party' and the expression 'park the car').

'Guwan git fukkered.'

'No', I coach. 'Garn git fukd.'

'Garren geet fukk.'

'Closer.'

'What is this in English?' he asks, handing me a piece of melon.

'Honeydew.'

'*I need you?*'

The idea of a fruit called I Need You pleases me on so many levels I pledge to keep it.

In the following weeks we lose all trace of English as I disappear into Adrien's world. He inducts me into his extended family, taking me to lunch at Séverine's cool younger sister's modern loft in Montmartre, and to dinner at her bourgeois older sister's penthouse near Trocadéro, with its spectacular view over the Eiffel Tower. There was a clock under it when I was an au pair, counting down the days to the millennium. Adrien remembers that too.

Weeks go by when I speak and listen to nothing but French. I no longer remember which language I'm speaking, and Adrien says I talk French in my sleep. When it becomes too hot in the daytime to sit outside, we stay in with the shutters closed, in underpants in front of his television set, having sex and watching everything from *Wife Swap* to French *Temptation Island* to dubbed versions of Adrien's boxed sets of Scorsese and Tarantino films, which I justify as all valuable language education. Séverine invites us to dinners and lunches in her air-conditioned salon, and even her French starts becoming clear to me. Like a photo developing in a darkroom, she becomes clearer too: more vulnerable than before, and softer, making more conversation with me and giving me the impression that we could be friends.

One mild August night she asks us over to share a summer *pot-au-feu* with a group of her cinema friends and Gigi, a sweet older gent who is 'best friends' with Séverine, but as far as I can see mainly listens to her problems and performs her errands. He pats my head and calls me *beauté* or *princesse*, which is nice in a grandfatherly way.

All are amazed I've never tried *pot-au-feu* before. 'I was vegetarian for a long time,' I tell them. The table goes silent.

'But why?' asks Julie, a petite brunette.

'It's hard to explain,' I say. 'I didn't like meat. I still don't think we need to eat it and that it's bad for the planet. But now I eat it, just a bit.'

Their faces remain blank.

'Well, in that case,' says Séverine, ladling a generous portion onto my plate. '*L'os à moelle.*'

I look down at the heavy piece of bone in front of me. Bone marrow? I look pleadingly at Adrien.

'You take a piece of toast,' he demonstrates, 'and you scoop out the marrow and smooth it on like this.' He raises the toast to his mouth, rubbing his tummy. 'See? Mmmm.'

The guests murmur, not taking their eyes off me. I put the grey goo in my mouth and swallow it down with a swig of red wine, suppressing the urge to retch. A beat. Then a roar of laughter and clapping.

'Bravo! Bravo!' says Gigi, coming over to kiss me. 'Welcome to delicious!'

'Do you like it?' asks Rémy, a man with a pencil moustache. The table goes silent. I search for a phrase that, to surprise them, will express that I loved it. And then it comes out:

'*C'est un truc de ouf quoi.*'

There's a pause. Then the entire room erupts in laughter. People bang on the table with forks and spoons. '*Ha ha, truc de ouf!*' Adrien is prouder than ever and Gigi says over and over, '*Elle est magnifique, MAGNIFIQUE!*' We laugh and laugh and clink glasses and talk and share and eat wondrous cheeses and an incredible *tarte tatin* made by Gigi's mother. Each time he mentions her a tear comes to his eye, and he looks down at his lap and puts his hands close to his body, as though she is dead and sacred, although she's alive and well and living in Courbevoie.

When we've finished eating, Séverine and Gigi clear the plates and we move back to the salon to drink *digestifs* and smoke more.

'So Jayne, tell me, what is your family heritage?' a short grey man named Gérard asks me. It's clear I've become the entertainment at this party, and the guests all smile at me as they find their comfortable positions on the couches, poufs and armchairs.

'Um, I don't know. English, Irish, Scottish. A bit of everything: Pioneers … I don't know much about it.'

The room stiffens.

I've never given my heritage much thought. And then it hits me: these people all know their history. They know they belong here. That the land is theirs. I'm not a native of Australia. I am ashamed of what my ancestors did to the indigenous people, and I felt terrible every day for living on their land. And yet I am not English or Irish or Scottish. I don't belong there either. And I have never travelled the real Australia, the centre. I've lived only a city life, sipping tea and tending my English garden, eating Asian food, Italian, Greek, Indian. The people at this table eat and speak French in France and *are* French.

I'm not *from* anywhere.

Yet, I feel more French than ever. My language is now a colourful pastiche of street Étienne, sultry Séverine, sweet Marie-France, cutting Lecoq teachers, and vulgar *Wife Swap* characters. But mostly I speak Adrien. His expressions, his shoulder raising and huffing, the way he rolls his 'r's and says *oui* sometimes on an in-breath. But also his argot, his high French, low French, French for the café, French for his friends, French for the hot-water guy on the telephone.

A few weeks after the *pot-au-feu* Adrien takes me to a concert in Bastille. Since that night at Séverine's, I've been enjoying the feeling that I'm disappearing into French, indetectable as a foreigner. But in the toilets when I ask a guy if there's any paper in the men's cubicle, he answers me in English.

'Out of interest,' I ask him in French, 'how did you know I speak English?'

'The smile in the voice,' he says, checking his teeth in the mirror.

I'm astounded and confused. Back at the bar I recount the story to Adrien. He laughs and says, 'Yes that's right, you have a smile when you talk.'

This is astonishing to me. I had no idea. As we walk down the busy canal back to my place I demand Adrien cure me of the smile. After I've said *bonjour* and *au revoir* at least fifty times he is exhausted.

'I'm sorry, but no matter how low you make your voice or how arrogant you sound, the smile is still there. Even when you sound angry you have the little smile.' He takes me in his arms. 'I like the smile.'

That's a nice thing to say. But how irritating not to be able to control my voice. I'm supposed to be an *actress*. I should be able to play this part.

'I don't want the smile,' I say, looking at my shoes and saying *bonjour* again.

'See? Even when you're sad you have the little smile.'

I try to frown at him, then mimic what he just said.

'You have too much enthusiasm in your voice,' he says. 'Try to speak as if you don't care.'

As if I don't care.

But I *do* care. Intrinsically. That's the problem.

I pledge to go deeper. I'll iron the goddamned Australia out of this body if it kills me.

My friends float back, first Kiki, then Nadine, and finally Harry, and Adrien and I spend more time at my place, lying on the cool floor, or at the canal with whoever's around, eating I Need You because it's cheap and delicious. On money days we wrap it in ham. Sometimes Raphaël and a few of Adrien's other friends join us, kicking off their espadrilles and untucking their shirts to fit in. We sprawl over the dirty banks on pieces of fabric and put cheeses and chips and cheap bottles of rosé on them, sharing cups. A man pushes a shopping cart around selling cold Tsingtao for two euros, and if we're lucky someone will have the foresight and bank balance to go over to Pink Flamingo and bring back fresh pizzas. We eat, drink, smoke and talk with our legs dangling over the water, musing about jumping in, Adrien with his neat jeans tucked up above his handsome ankles, Harry in his array of '80s board shorts, Kiki in her long beaded skirts, Nadine in cute vintage wear. Kiki brings me a bag of old dresses and I pin them in around the boob area and wear them with a pair of thongs Nadine was going to throw out. We are definitely bobos, except probably Adrien with his clean shirts and boat shoes.

During the day we sometimes walk up to the Buttes-Chaumont and sit under a tree by the stream: the feeling of my feet in water and on grass gives me a feeling I hadn't realised I'd missed, the simple connection with nature and the vibrations of the earth beneath all that concrete. It brings out a yearning in me for fields and beaches, stretches of emptiness, but even a train ticket out of Paris is beyond our reach. Anyway, Harry says that Deauville, the nearest beach to Paris, is like swimming in dishwater.

One stifling day, when Adrien is at an audition, I'm at the canal in a deep conversation with Nadine when I notice a guy climb over the barrier on the top of the Bridge of Atmosphère and start taking his clothes off. Harry.

'Jesus ... *no!*' shouts Nadine, and the entire crowd of bobos looks up to stare. There has been much speculation as to what lies beneath the murky green depths of the canal – dead bodies, shopping trolleys, pets, bikes, car parts, toilet seats and a lot of rat skeletons is the word. But I understand Harry's thinking: on days like today, with beer-blurred eyes and heat stroke, the water can look like a crystalline Swiss lake. Still, I agree with Nadine and call, 'Don't j—'

Too late. The crowd gasps. I pray he's not dead, or skewered on something. But then he's up, smiling, and swimming towards the bank. Women rush to him; he's now a local hero, the stupidest man in town. There's no sign of embarrassment or shock on Harry's face, he is wholly glad he did it. He looks refreshed, if gooey, and in no hurry to get out. Pushing himself off the grimy wall, he backstrokes into the middle of the canal, to a chorus of cheers.

Nadine and I accompany him back to his place to drink beer while he takes a shower, and to make sure there's no lasting damage. Once Nadine is satisfied he'll survive, she takes off to meet her date, and Harry asks me to stay: he's got leftover chicken curry, and *Rebel Without a Cause* is on Arte tonight – dubbed, of course. In French it's *The Fury of Living*. When it's over he gets up to serve dinner.

'Do you know who your ancestors were?' I ask from his kitchen bench.

'Irish, English. White folk. Murderers. Why?'

'I know both my grandmothers had Scottish maiden names, McLean and McPherson. My surname is Tuttle – my Irish friend says that's not a weird name there. My nan made a family tree that goes way back to England. But that's all I know. And isn't a tree, like, a tree? It forks and it forks, even a few branches up. How can you get a true idea of your identity?'

'You can't. You can follow one branch, I suppose, and see where it leads.'

'That's what Nan did. Do you feel weird here for being so British and coming from Australia?'

'No. Yeah. I dunno.'

'It just feels so strange. We're from there, but we're not. How many Aboriginal people do you know?'

'I know loads. I spend time in the Kimberley every time I go back. I spent six months there once making a doco. I know some Elders.'

'See, I've never made that effort. I don't know anything about the land. Basic warped Australian history from school, that's all. I feel so English. I like cities! It feels like home here. But why?'

'You're talking weird,' Harry says. 'But go on.'

I tell him about Séverine's friends being so disappointed I couldn't tell them anything about my heritage.

Harry laughs and takes our plates to the living room. '*Putes et criminels*. Want another beer?'

'What do you mean?'

He hands me a Kronenbourg. 'Whores and convicts, that's all they want to hear.'

'Really?'

'The French are obsessed by heritage. What family you're from, what region, what name. There's nothing of interest to them about Australia other than kangaroos and Aborigines and the fact that we're descended from whores and convicts. Can I take your photo?'

'But the ancestors on Nan's chart were wealthy settlers. Although I'm sure some of them must have stolen a loaf of bread.'

'Code for whore. Don't fight it.'

He lights my cigarette and snaps a photo of me with his Polaroid.

'Anyway, it's great to be Australian,' he says, flapping the sticky piece of paper around and placing it on the arm of the chair before taking another one. 'Not to have all that bogged-downness of history. The world likes us. Imagine what it's like being American or English here. One of the Americans at my work got spat on in the street the other day just for speaking out loud. We're seen as harmless. Our country is too far away to have any significance to anyone in the world, though our fuckwit of a prime minister might think we're a major player. I reckon we're lucky. No responsibility. No weight.'

He hands me the two photos. Against the picture of desert landscape on the wall behind me, my head looks like Uluṟu.

'Will you go back one day?' I ask.

'Hell yeah,' says Harry. 'I'd be there in two seconds if I could get directing work. Life's so much better there. The surf, the air. And easier. You've only been here a year, you'll see. It gets stifling. You start to need the air and the sun. The wild.'

I consider this as I kiss him goodbye. He gives me a slightly longer hug than usual, which feels nice in a brotherly way. He pins one of the photos to his wall with a collection of other random faces and I put the other one in my pocket.

The canal is quiet. A piece of tissue paper is caught in a tree. The lights are on in the apartments along the water and my outsider feeling returns stronger than ever, that feeling of detachment, the balloon untethered.

─────

Adrien's financial situation grows dire, so he takes a job at the FNAC, the audiovisual chain store near Odéon. At least it's air-conditioned there. Kiki is busy preparing for a show, so I go to Nadine's and play gin rummy, or hang around the canal and the Récollets, trying not to spend money. August gets even hotter. My kitchen is overrun by ants. The playground downstairs is quiet and the park overtaken by party people playing loud techno music all night long.

Kiki calls one day and tells me to meet her at the Petit Château d'Eau – she has good news. I am in a thrift store trying on a pink two-euro tank that smells of mothballs and someone else's sweat, but looks good. Silk, perhaps, or probably polyester. Whatever it is, it makes my nipples stick out and I elect to keep it on and not wear a bra, because why not.

A hot breeze teases my hair as I pedal along the rue des Petites-Écuries. The sun is going down and people are spilling out onto the pavements, standing around tables and leaning on poles, laughing, arguing, drinking. I take my feet off the pedals as I draw nearer the Faubourg-Saint-Denis, where the bike lane becomes blocked by music fans queuing to enter the New Morning jazz club. I weave my way past them and into the intersection, where a cloud of fragrant weed hits my lungs. I breathe it in deep. Traffic comes at me from three directions, from the rue du Château d'Eau to the east and from the north and south on Saint-Denis. I wobble my way through the chaos, narrowly avoiding a woman pushing a pram and the rear bumper of a car as it pulls up short. My brakes are hopeless so I use my sandals on the road. I pull back into the bike lane and proceed the wrong way up it into little Africa and its buzzing hairdressing salons with people crammed in having their hair braided and twisted and sprayed and coloured. Balls of hair in the gutter spring into my spokes as I roll over them with my crappy tyres. Shops sell wigs in pink, yellow, brown, black, white, grey, blond, sparkly purple and fluorescent green, in every style and shape you could imagine, on white plastic heads with names like Bella and Lucie and Diamant and Kama and Star and Trixie.

At the boulevard de Sébastopol I hear a bell ding and someone call, 'Jayne!' It's Étienne. We stop in front of a man grilling corn on a barbecue and Étienne kisses me on both cheeks. *'Félicitations!'*

'Toi aussi!'

It's the first time I've seen him since we were both accepted into second year. He looks tanned, his curly dark hair fairer from time in the sun.

He complements my *vingt mouvements*, telling me they were *truc de ouf quoi*. I laugh my head off. He smiles and pays for his corn cob, and is swept away in the Friday night crowd. I stop for a moment and stare at my reflection in the broken mirror outside the Sunshine fashion shop. My face and body are splintered into chunks of hair and flesh and the bright, swirling colours of the world behind me.

I turn my bike around and glide through the bumper-to-bumper traffic, past the coolest African eatery in town, which I have never seen closed or empty. Drum music thumps, people dance and slap hands amid the spit and graffiti and the rubbish squashed into the pavement. I pedal up the boulevard, narrowly missing motorbikes and scooters and a smart car as I manoeuvre into the bike lane. Past the imposing Mairie with its authoritative turrets and towers, past the Firemen's Caserne and on to the picturesque bar, Le Petit Château d'Eau, where I step off my bike and chain it to a pole.

Two well-built *pompiers*, the local firemen-studs who attend to all neighbourhood emergencies, walk past me on their way back to the Caserne and say *bonsoir*. A group of well-dressed young women sit drinking kir outside the bar and I look for Kiki, finding her inside in one of the old rustic booths, nursing a glass of beer and a little bowl of peanuts.

'*Bella regazza!*' she says, kissing and hugging me. It feels like ages since we've seen each other.

I order a beer too, and we clink glasses and drink. Momo, the dog who lives in the bar, comes and sits under my seat. I pat him gently.

'So what's the news?'

Zahir's gone and Kiki has been nailing the yoga teacher. And the yoga teacher, whose name is Manu, teaches a famous photographer, who was an addict for many years and now requires a special diet and support. She has given Kiki a job as her personal chef and assistant.

'That's the best news I've ever heard,' I say, banging on the table.

'She's incredible,' says Kiki. 'And it means that even though my residency at the Cité is nearly up, I can stay in Paris and work. It's perfect.'

My stomach clenches at the mere mention of Kiki leaving. I haven't been able to fathom it as an option. Now I don't have to. 'Praise the lord!'

'And that's not all,' she says, leaning over the table.

The famous photographer had booked to spend the summer at an expensive health retreat in Florida, but Kiki has convinced her to spend the money on a two-week holiday in the Dordogne instead. Manu will teach yoga, Kiki will cook, 'and you,' she adds, 'will entertain! Oh, and drive. None of us want to do that.'

I jump for joy. 'The countryside!'

'Are you wearing a bra?'

'Fresh air!'

'I dream of not having to wear a bra.'

'Let's drink more beer!'

'Wait!' she says. 'I brought us a surprise.' She reaches down into her bag and brings up a magnum of Dom Pérignon.

'Norbert!'

'It wouldn't fit in my fridge, so it's warm, but it'll still be good!'

'Yay!'

'Let's go to the canal and drink it from plastic cups!'

The bobos are at the canal in droves, in effortless flowing clothes, with baskets of wine and cheese, and music. Drummers drum and dancers dance; the trees have all their leaves back on and the sun pokes its last rays through them, trying to push away the creeping evening coolness. A young guy on a skateboard lights my cigarette and Kiki and I drink the frothy delicacy of Dom Pérignon from our cups.

'Life is good!' I splutter.

'*La vita e bella!*'

'*La vita e bella!*' I repeat. 'Why so Italian today?'

'I don't know. Today feels like Italy.'

Today is Italy but we are in France and are Australian so we drink the entire bottle of champagne and dance our way up the cobblestoned path by the canal, through the hazy mass of bodies and down the rue des Récollets, around Piss Alley beside the Église Saint-Laurent as the bells toll. The sky is prussian blue as we cross the busy intersection of Magenta and Strasbourg and make our way down the rue de la Fidélité, past a darkened bar with tiger-skin couches.

'*Bar-à-putes*,' I say, pointing to it with a wink.

'It's not a whore bar,' says Kiki. 'It's just full of old cougars.'

'Adrien reckons it is.'

'Adrien would.'

A pause.

'Do you like Adrien?' I ask.

'Of course!' she says. 'But I can imagine why he would think something like this is a whore bar.'

I'm not sure what she means but I don't pursue it. I feel giddy on life, on this night, and I want to drink it in with my best friend.

The rue du Faubourg-Saint-Denis is like a festival; music and laughter blend with the clinking of crockery and glassware on the terraces. At the end of the street the golden glow of the ancient arch beckons us down to the Mauri7, but Kiki spots a cab, hugs me and falls into it, and I couldn't have drunk more anyway, so I stumble up the street, past the refugees singing in the square, towards the gates of the Récollets, shining in the moonlight.

I tap in the code but I'm too drunk to go to bed, so I turn and walk back down to the canal, where the world is paisley and people are everywhere. I sit on my own, with them all.

Tits of the Dordogne

Adrien can't take time off his job and isn't invited to the Dordogne anyway, so I kiss him goodbye after dinner on my floor, pack a little bag and sit around feeling nervous about meeting such a famous artist.

When I showed Adrien a book of her photography I borrowed from Kiki, it flopped open at an image of a naked guy masturbating. She had captured the moment so truthfully – the clenched jaw, the flushed cheeks, the vein pulsating in his forehead – it made me excited and a bit sick at the same time.

'Nooo!' said Adrien, shielding his eyes.

'Really? What about these?' I flipped through pages I'd marked, photos of people with vacant eyes in shabby bedrooms, naked couples kissing, children in living rooms, drag queens in a backyard. Al, the photographer, had this way of bringing you right up close into people's lives. Too close. That's why I loved them. They were hard to look at, yet you couldn't look away.

'I don't like these photos. *C'est glook.*'

I didn't know what *glook* meant but could feel it from the way it sounded – seedy, dark, grim. Of course they were. That was the point. They were unabashedly real, with their harsh, realistic colours, trashy decor, and blurred, off-centre framing. They revealed a deep, painful beauty. I was startled by his rejection of them, but put the book down and changed the subject. What did it matter if we had different taste in art?

Al lives in the rue Charlot. I ride there in the summer rain, which turns my hair into a wild fuzzy mane. Manu is to take her on the one-o'clock train from Montparnasse, because she doesn't like cars or planes, and Kiki and I will pick up a rental car and drive to the château. I am the designated driver.

Manu lets me in. I have only met him once, after Kiki's yoga class one day. He is in the same stretched T-shirt and hippie pants with bells around the bottoms, but his long matted hair this time is pulled into a bun. We kiss each other and he says he's glad I'm coming. Then he gets distracted and disappears, leaving me in a large, cluttered salon with light streaming in dusty stripes across the exotic rugs and worn sofas with beautiful cats on them. People emerge from various corners: a beautiful, smoking androgyne with cropped black hair points me down the hall, past a guy with a naked washboard stomach who gives me a slow hug like he hasn't seen me in years, leading to Kiki, fussing over Al in her bed, a middle-aged baby bird in a pile of sweaty sheets. Kiki squeezes me, mumbles something and rushes out of the room.

'Hello … sweetie,' Al drawls, reaching out to caress my face. 'Aren't you beautiful? Your hair. Can I photograph you, sweetie? While we're on vacation?'

'Of course,' I say, flattered, helping her to a sitting position. It feels like I already know her – perhaps because she's in bed. She is overweight but fragile. Her hair is ginger with thick strands of grey wiring their way from the crown into clumps in the middle of her back. She looks exhausted.

'Kiki!' she calls, and Kiki comes barrelling back into the room, hands full of linen and clothes. 'Darling. Can we bring Rosie?'

Kiki hesitates. 'Sure, Al. Does she have a cage thing?'

'Yeah, sweetie. I take her everywhere.'

Rosie, Al's favourite cat, is asleep on a sumptuous velvet chair in the salon. She does not like being woken and she does not like the cage. The half-naked guy helps us try to get her into it but she lashes out and scratches him on the midriff. He laughs and leaves the room, gazing down at the scratch like it's something exquisite.

The drive takes almost a whole day and my driving is scary, but we finally pull up around midnight beside an up-lit château with a dark forest beyond it, and leap out, silently screaming with delight, running across the vast lawns, arms spread, faces wild. An owl hoots and we stop and listen to it, gazing around at the sleeping château with its stone walls covered in ivy, its high windows and moulded turrets.

Kiki takes my hand and we creak open the kitchen door and run barefoot across the wooden floors; there are huge fireplaces and a dining room with ghostly chandeliers and big soft sofas and big clean bathrooms with big deep baths in them. Kiki spins in the kitchen with its ten-burner stove and huge wooden table and beautiful pots and pans strung up *à l'ancienne*.

Manu's and Al's bags are strewn around the table. Kiki gets a bottle of white wine from the fridge and we take our glasses to one of the giant sofas and sprawl on it. Outside is black. There are stars. A thumbnail moon. We drink the whole bottle and fall asleep.

The first days pass in a blissful haze. Kiki and I are constantly drunk and full of excitement. It's as if we've been set free after being cooped up too long. Al has brought a bag of her favourite rare films and we lie around and watch them in the salon, Al watching us watch them and loving that we love them. We go to the village markets and the wine store and Al buys expensive vintage champagne, though she doesn't drink. We feast like barons in the vast dining room with its long, old wooden table, Al beaming as she watches us devour it all, content with her bowl of lentils and can of Diet Coke. We play backgammon and go for long walks through the countryside and lie on the lawn in the sun. Manu gives yoga classes on the warm wooden floor of the master bedroom. We go on missions to find things to photograph, like weird topiary gardens, and animals and children and trees. Al is inspired and takes hundreds of photos, of Kiki in the kitchen, Manu in the hammock, Rosie pawing a bird, Manu and Kiki kissing, Kiki in the bath, and all of us lying on the sofas and me in front of the TV wearing the 'Jane Likes Dick' T-shirt Jack gave me.

One afternoon Al grabs her camera and leads Kiki and me, giddy on champagne, to a part of the forest she has found at the bottom of the property and suggests we take off our shirts. We laugh – why not? And it *is* funny – Kiki's boobs are so big and round and mine are so small, and she is so curvy and dark and I am so rake-like and blond, and we frolic like drunken nymphs as Al snaps the shots. When she loses interest in us and starts taking photos of the dying light in the tops of the trees, we pull our shirts on and crawl back up to the garden. Manu comes and sits with us but can't break into our silly mood and eventually wanders away.

Al is a range of people throughout the day. Sweet Al. Laughing Al. Quiet Al. Delirious Al. Incoherent Al. Content Al. Restless Al. Playful Al. My favourite Al is Cuddly Al, tucked up in bed wanting to talk all night about stories and ideas and art and parents and friendship and love and nightmares.

'Isn't it hard to make work that's so close to you?' I ask one night as she is snuggled in her blankets. 'Don't the people in your photographs get angry at you?'

'Of course,' she says, playing with my hair. 'But if you're going to make real art, you have to be ready to hurt people. Being an artist is painful.'

'I'm terrified of upsetting people.'

'Well, you'd better not be an artist then, sweetie.'

She turns over and I pat her hair. 'Bring me some of your writing. Read to me.'

I bring back my computer and, embarrassed, start reading the stuff I'm prouder of, the love rants about Adrien, a play idea about two sisters. Al lies silent, asleep perhaps, but I keep reading. I come to a piece about Mum, a long passage called 'I'm Sorry, We Still Have Time'. The writing is ghastly, ill-formed and raw: it makes me want to be sick just looking at it. I read the words softly, hoping Al is asleep, horrified at what I've written, like I've betrayed my family and Mum's experience by even attempting to put words around it.

As I'm tiptoeing out Al mumbles, 'That's where it is, sweetie. That place.'

'Really?' I whisper.

'Hmm. That place.'

⁓

Al's moods stay mostly sweet for the next few days but start to become spliced with more frequent dark moments. By the seventh day the sweetness has all but disappeared. It's clear she's a lot more unwell than we realised, and still dealing with the after-effects of long-term addiction. She sleeps terribly, and in the mornings can't feel her legs and screams in terror; by lunchtime she is calm but restless, and the rest of the day her mood shifts between reclusiveness and listlessness to outbursts of anger. She starts to lash out and snap at us; the colour in Kiki's cheeks starts to drain, and Manu walks out of their yoga session one day and stands on the lawn for a long time, breathing.

One night, Al appears at the top of the staircase as I'm walking past.

'Hi Al!' I say. 'Are you okay? Can I bring you something?'

'What are you doing here?' she snarls. 'Go home! FREELOADER!'

Manu comes from the living room and looks up at Al. She hobbles back to her room and slams the door.

'I think I should go,' I say.

Manu sighs. 'It's not you. She's not well.'

Kiki agrees I should go – for my own sake, but also to give Al fewer targets to abuse. She convinces me they'll be okay, and drops me the next morning at the station with the cat, who sprays and moans all the way back to Paris.

My Studio of Good never felt so good. I dump my things and let Rosie out of the cage, praying Chantal doesn't find out. The cat goes straight to the shower and shits in it, digging at imaginary dirt to cover it up. I go upstairs and flop gratefully onto my bed. E.T. says hi.

'Why didn't you call?' asks Adrien when I phone him. 'I was worried.'

'There was no reception. I missed you.'

'No reception?' He pauses. 'Was it fun?'

'Yes. No. When can I see you?'

'I'm busy tonight. Tomorrow. Why was it not fun?'

I tell him about Al's addiction and how we didn't realise how unwell she is.

'Did you take drugs?'

'No.'

'Did she take photos of you?'

'No,' I lie.

Guilt gnaws at my bones when we hang up. I'm not sure why I felt the need to lie about the photos. Telling him would only make him want to see them, and I'm not sure he'd see the humour in them. He doesn't understand Al's aesthetic, and he's questioned Kiki's sexuality, so why provoke something? But lying to him sits uneasily in my bones. Why do I keep telling him these little lies?

Rosie leaps onto the end of the bed and stares at me with her head cocked before coming to curl up with me. I am grateful, though she makes my eyes itch.

Four days later I get a call from Kiki. 'The bitch is back,' she says. They have cut the trip short.

I take the métro to Oberkampf with Rosie. Manu answers the door looking beaten-up.

He kisses me. 'Al is in the salon. She's been asking about you.'

Rosie jumps from her cage and goes running inside. 'Rosie, darling!' I hear Al purr. I don't want to go in, but she calls my name. I walk to the edge of the salon, where she's sprawled on a chaise longue in her pyjamas, smoking.

'Jayne, sweetie, come here.'

I go and sit reluctantly next to her, like a three-year-old. She is afternoon oozy Al. 'Manu tells me I said some things. Sorry, sweetie, I don't really remember. I don't think I was feeling well.'

'I shouldn't have drunk all that wine and stuff. I didn't need to. I just —'

'Shhh, sweetie, come here. It's all fine.'

I put my head on her thick, strangely comforting shoulder and she strokes my head. For some annoying reason I begin to cry.

'Paulina!' she calls. 'Bring the photos from today. Paulina!'

The androgyne comes rushing in with an orange envelope.

'These are for you, sweetie,' oozes Al. 'They're beautiful. If we use them, the studio will call you. I love them. You and Kiki are sooo beautiful.'

I thank her and leave, opening the envelope by the canal, careful who might be looking over my shoulder. The photos are funny but I hate them so much I want to throw them in the water. I take them to Kiki's.

She moans at the sight of me. I hug her.

'I just took the cat back.'

'How was the slut-hole?'

'In afternoon happy phase. She gave me the photos.'

Kiki tears them out of my hands and sits down. A crazed laugh bursts from her as she looks at the shot of her and Manu kissing in bed. 'Yuk,' she says, flopping backwards. She seems drunk. 'I like these secret garden lesbo ones. Look at your sweet little nipples!' She tosses the photos aside and covers her face with her hands.

'What are you going to do?' I say.

'I quit,' she says. 'Of course.'

My throat tightens. 'So what will you do now?'

'Do my show then go, I suppose. I don't know. I have to move out of here soon. I was going to look for a place, but now …'

'You'll really go home?' I try to mask the panic in my voice.

'I think so. I miss my studio – I'm tired of sleeping where I paint. And I want babies. Not now, but soon. And I miss the sea! Don't you?'

'No,' I say, seeing home flash before my eyes. 'I don't miss the sea at all.'

Back in Black

My black school clothes are looser after the loss of muscle tone over summer. Our reduced group of thirty feels strange at first and we stand looking at each other, assessing the gaps, survivors of some war. We need to recalibrate but there's no time; as in first year, we are catapulted into action like highly trained robots. This year we're at ground level, exploring the grand theatrical territories of comedy, tragedy, buffoonery, the absurd and the grotesque. We organise ourselves immediately into groups for *autocours*, according to the strengths we now know well in each other. I make a pact to try to work with new people instead of the small company that was naturally forming between me, Faye, Meg, Ravi, Étienne and Marie-France.

Marie-France pouts at me as I move off towards Marc Finland. Thank goodness Marc New York didn't get through, or Marcs Northern England, Denmark, Seattle or France. Now I can just call him Marc. There's only one double now: Sarahs Israel and England. But there's no trouble telling them apart: the former is six feet tall and the latter a dormouse.

Kiki's exhibition is on the third Thursday night of term. Friday is still *autocours* performance day and the looks I get when I cut out of rehearsal are so dark they could kill. Tomorrow we will be murdered. But I would rather get kicked in the shins by Étienne and slaughtered by Angela than miss Kiki's show.

The night air is cool when I mount the métro steps at Pont Marie, and the long bland façade of Cité des Arts looks almost beautiful, its utilitarian windows reflecting the lights along the Seine. The sound of voices and clinking glass spills from the downstairs gallery, whose nondescript white box has been transformed into a world of colour by Kiki. She is in the corner in a red sequinned dress talking to a small group, and I can see Nadine and Harry and some of Kiki's other friends from the Cité moving around the space, taking in the paintings of misty rivers and floating trees, houses, windows, rain.

Adrien is in the centre of the room, transfixed by a triptych in watery greens and blues and browns. The colours, he says, remind him of the house in Fontainebleau where he lived with his mother for a while when he was little. We kiss and walk around the show together, spending time in front of each piece. I have seen them all before, but watching Adrien look at them gives them new life.

There is champagne and light music and I keep expecting there to be a speech but it doesn't come. I drink two glasses of champagne, which makes me dizzy as I've barely eaten all day – since school began, meals have been rare, there just isn't time. Adrien pulls me outside and we kiss and smoke.

After the gallery closes a group of us go up to Kiki's studio and drink vodka pommes and more champagne to loud music. The room gets crammed as residents from the Cité file in and people's bodies become looser. Harry moves the furniture to the walls to make a dance floor, and Kiki's party playlist gets everyone wiggling and jumping around. I finally spy an opening and corner her.

'You're a raving success!' I slur. 'You can never go home!'

She smiles and hugs me.

'Oh love, I have to go.'

'No you don't! You have a following here now. You can't abandon your following!'

She hugs me tight. Then Nadine hugs us hugging. A whole lot of other people join in. Then I'm being spun around by an Asian guy wearing pyjamas, then I'm dancing with Harry and he's making me laugh with his stupid moves. The dancing and laughter continue for so long it takes me a while to notice that Adrien isn't in the room.

Sometime after midnight he walks back in. The party is winding down and people are splitting off to nightclubs and bars, onto bikes, into the night. Kiki and I are scooping scraps into a garbage bag.

'Where have you been?' I ask.

'For a walk,' he says.

We decide to walk to Châtelet to get two taxis, as he has to work tomorrow. It's a clear night, the last remnants of summer hanging on just tightly enough to make me not regret leaving my doodoona in the cupboard. The moon is full and bright, illuminating the edges of the clouds. The bars are closing, the streets quiet.

'Let's sit by the river for a moment,' I suggest. 'It's too pretty to go home.'

We walk across to the Île Saint-Louis and hoist our legs over the bank. His shoes are smooth and pointy and tap together lightly. My sneakers are grimy.

'Are you jealous?' he asks out of the blue.

'Of what?' I ask. 'Of whom?' My heart speeds up. Has he been with someone else? Is that why he disappeared earlier in the night?

'No, I mean, are you *jealous*.' It takes a long time for me to establish he means jealous by nature, and not of something specific. I tell him I'm not at all, I never have been. I've always thought that if someone wants something else, well then, they should have it.

'Why, did something happen?' I ask. My mind is spinning.

'No, of course not.'

I have no idea where this is leading.

'I'm jealous,' he interrupts as I go to speak, as though it's something he needs to get off his chest.

'But why? I don't understand.'

He says he just is. Just jealous.

I don't know what to say. It feels like a threat.

He turns and looks at me. There is something definite in his eye. I scan the landscape of his face in the lamplight, the prominence of his cheeks, the sprouting grass of his sideburns, the line of his jaw, tight. He wants to own me. A deep fear throbs in me, dredging up an unfamiliar lust. You caveman. Owning me. Clubbing anyone who comes near. My blood runs hot and thick with danger, my insides are a freefall, like one of Kiki's paintings.

The kiss has a primal feeling to it, like he's letting me see his insides. It's not so pretty in there, not so cardboard cut-out. It scares me, but my skin sizzles and my heart pounds. I want it.

Bird on a Cob

If I stand outside Kiki's door long enough, perhaps she won't go. A woman mopping the floor moves closer to me, before stopping and giving me a pointed look. I have to go in.

She is sitting on the windowsill looking out over the river, where the trees are almost bare again. I take off my doodoona and hang it on the door handle, its shoulders slumping like mine. The studio is almost bare too, except for a big purple suitcase.

'Look at those fuckwits,' she says, pointing at a group of tourists walking along the quai, licking Berthillon ice-creams in the icy wind, coats up around their ears.

'If it's pear and blackberry they're not insane.'

'Coffee and tiramisu …'

'Don't go, there's ice-cream!' Tears come.

'Don't, you'll make me cry.'

We hug for a long time.

'I'll be back,' she says, turning to me and brushing the dust off her skirt. 'You'll be Madame Masson with little baby croissants running around.'

'Don't wait *that* long,' I say.

She doesn't want me to come with her to the station, but I scamper along anyway like a nervous puppy, trying to be of use, cramping her. The escalator down to her train is very long and I watch her slow descent from the other side of the turnstile. After the initial wave and blown kisses it is awkward – all she can do is shift on her step and let me watch her. I keep waving until she has no feet, no legs, no body, no head.

Gone.

I stare into space, listening to the world going on as normal around me, until a woman with a pram hits my ankle. I limp out to the rue de Dunkerque, grateful for the pain, but it's not enough to break me from the fog. My chest is rigid as I walk in the grey day towards the boulevard de Magenta, knowing that if anything should enter my cloud between here and home I shall shatter to the ground, like the window pane we've practised at school. It could be a smile, a slight trip on the concrete, or even the sky opening up a fraction. It happens to be a bird. Outside the Terminus Nord. Or what was once a bird. A bloated, perfectly intact feathered body with just the bloody red spike of its spine coming out the top, where its head should be: a sort of candied-apple bird on a stick. A bird on the cob. I don't understand how the bird got like that. Tears sputter from my eyes, my nose, my mouth.

People cry here, in the streets. It's okay to cry in the street. Before spring broke last year, the grey winter days drew on so long people would simply walk around crying. They also fight in the streets. They shout. I am crying loudly now, in the street. I make no effort to stop.

I walk down the boulevard in a daze. A man is passed out on the steps of the Marché Saint-Quentin, his hands and feet black and crusted over, a wet line trickling from beneath him down the steps. I cry and cry and cry. A little girl swipes past me on her scooter. I drift into the bike lane and a loud *ding* jolts me back onto the pavement.

I buy a packet of Marlboro lights and smoke one outside La Strasbourgeoise, watching the waiters in their traditional black-and-whites dash in and out, opening bottles of Orangina and beer, handing out little bowls of pretzels, emptying ashtrays. One of them asks if I want a table. He calls me *mademoiselle*.

Back in my studio I lie on the bed and stare at the rafter. The moth is gone from the ceiling, gone on with its life, moving forward. Or dead, probably. I remember a funny poem I read about a moth saying that fire is beautiful, and that he'd prefer to singe himself on a cigar lighter for one moment of beauty than live a long life of nothing much. I'd forgotten that poem until now. For some reason it comforts me. When Chris dumped me before I first came to Paris, I told Mum I would never love anyone again. I had decided I would go through life contentedly without love, because if love had to go then it wasn't worth having in the first place.

She disagreed with a passion. 'But love is all there is!' she said. 'You have to love hard. Love as hard as you can. Even if it goes, having love, even for a short time, is worth more than a lifetime of not loving.'

I swore the same thing to myself after she died. To lose people is too hard, I thought; better not to love at all.

Kiki leaving is like losing another layer of skin. But I'm not sorry for loving her.

Thirty

In the 'Make us Cry' *autocours*, I make everyone laugh. In 'Make us Laugh', I make everyone silent, except Claude, who gives a loud sigh. But I am working something out. I like the place between tragic and funny – that awkward place where you're not sure whether to laugh or cry. Though we flunk a series of *autocours* together, Marie-France, Faye, Meg and Sarah (and sometimes Étienne) are all into the same thing. For the next *autocours*, instead of being so intent on following the rules, we branch out into a new, weird place that feels risky, and the result is far from successful but the teachers see something building and encourage us to explore it further. We smash together different kinds of text and create scripts with funny parts, silly and painful parts, using the tragic chorus and acrobatics and even song to make mad little pieces that make no sense. It doesn't matter. An aesthetic is coming – we can all feel it. And we're having fun.

Late one Friday night at the Mauri7 I need to pee. I stumble down the grotty staircase to the festering bathroom, but the queue is long and I can't wait so I run out into the freezing night to the kebab shop, ordering hot chips to soak up the alcohol as I run to the back of the shop.

Back at the bar with my chips, revived, I squeeze onto the banquette next to Marc, who helps himself to a fistful. Faye is laughing so hard at something she is holding her stomach, eyes streaming with tears. Tim sets down a round of beers. Glasses chink, Étienne says *santé*, I light another cigarette and suck the salt from between my thumb and finger, glancing up at the clock behind the bar. The skinny hand disappears behind the big hand on twelve.

I have just turned thirty.

Such an ugly number. Adrien can't say it. He can't put his tongue in the 'th' position, it seems rude and makes him horny. It makes me horny too, seeing his tongue come out of his mouth like that.

I leave the bar and walk out into the night. The street is calmer than usual and the icy air sobers me up a bit as I stumble up the street. A pasty moon hides above the buildings like a milky cheese. The métro rumbles beneath my feet; all those corridors and rails and people, all these nationalities, all this time passing. At the Récollets I stop halfway up the stairs and put my cheek against the cold, sure, stone wall.

Adrien makes the mistake of taking me for my birthday dinner to a restaurant along the quai near the Cité, where Kiki and I used to go for drinks. I've avoided going anywhere near the Cité since she left: any place that evokes a memory of her makes me ache.

Her ghost at the table near the doorway keeps me preoccupied for the entire meal, frustrating Adrien.

'I'm sorry, my love,' I tell him as we eat a dessert of warm *tarte tatin*. 'I'm just distracted with school and everything.'

'You're distracted a lot lately,' he says, putting his hand on mine.

We go back to my place and I die by surprise as he is experiencing a cataclysmic passing. There is something operatic about his death. Mine was a shock, I don't normally die like that. We hold each other tight afterwards, like we've just saved each other from falling over a cliff.

⌁

Adrien's play is a success. It's one of those ones where the actors start their roles while you're drinking wine in the foyer, so as Raph, Séverine and I chat, we are harassed by strung-out teenagers begging for money, and mentally ill people asking for cigarettes. The play is performed in the round and we sit on the floor as the troupe act out the devised piece, mixing text from various writers on youth and suicide and drugs. The young woman playing Adrien's girlfriend straddles and writhes on him so convincingly I feel a strange jealousy prickle up my back and kind of like it. I tell him later and it turns us both on so much we kill ourselves passionately on each other.

Adrien is very good in the awful play and some agents and directors see him and he starts getting more interesting auditions for film roles and theatre. But still he mostly gets cast in TV commercials and magazine spreads, and needs to supplement it all with his boring job at the FNAC store, which emasculates him so much he won't let me come and visit. They make him wear a little yellow vest.

My work at school intensifies to the point where I have no time to think of anything but rehearsals. Towards the end of the spring term, the class sits in Chez Jeannette with dead eyes: we have nothing left. The first-years chat and giggle like they don't know the pain of existence. Sarah Israel begins crying over nothing. Nobody comforts her. We are zombified.

For the term presentation, several of my pieces have been selected to be performed, which is the greatest tick you can get. There's a mysterious moving sculpture that gives birth to itself; a woman having a meltdown inside herself, on the level of Greek tragedy; a redheaded cabaret idiot; an absurd gynaecologist. The performances are the most satisfying acting I have done in my life. Nadine and Adrien clap loudly in their seats.

That night I want to pick every piece apart with Adrien, but he is intent on being polite and positive.

'Come on,' I beg him. 'Give it to me straight.'

But he doesn't have more to say and gets a little defensive.

I think about what Al said and wonder whether I have pushed hard enough, or far enough, into the uncomfortable place. I don't know. I guess that means I haven't.

The Fury of Living

Christmas in Normandy is quick, sweet and full of strange seafood, like sea urchins. Seafood in French is 'sea fruits'. There are little shells that you use tiny forks for, extracting little creatures that look like snot. I've never been able to afford seafood, so I guzzle it all up, even the snot, which tastes excellent.

I meet Adrien's grandmother, Georgette, who sits all day at her living-room window, looking out at an old gnarled tree, naming the birds that are, or will be, or have been, in it. I also meet Jacques, her second husband, who looks like Santa Claus. Adrien's family is sweet and kind; his aunt gives me a hot water bottle in the shape of a love heart. Séverine gives Adrien and me year-long memberships to the Louvre. The snow is magical. We stay for the feast on Christmas Eve, but the next afternoon, after lunch and a walk in the forest, we hightail it back to Paris. Adrien has to work.

It feels good to be back in Paris, and I spend a few days with Adrien, celebrating New Year's Eve at Thérèse's party in her parents' huge modern flat in Neuilly. Then I go back to the Récollets: Tatiana has asked me to help out with Miru while they prepare for his dad's show. Makoto does installation art, and for his opening they have another babysitter for Miru, so I can come.

It's weird to go to an art thing without Kiki. Adrien's got the play, but a big group from the Récollets are going, so I throw my leg over the back of Lamine's motorbike and whiz through the rainy streets, past dim lamps and looming façades, swerving through the narrow streets of the Marais and up the rue de Rivoli to the grand Ministry of Culture in the rue Saint-Honoré, with its gleaming metallic exterior.

Makoto's installation is a light-and-sound show in an elevator: each level is a different experience. I like the third floor disco and dance a little in the squashed cabin, then want to get out. In the main gallery there is furniture stuck to the walls, and a giant skull in the centre made of stainless-steel pots and pans. Sleek French people guzzle expensive champagne and eat fish things in pastry.

Lamine disappears. Tatiana goes off with Makoto. I find myself staring at a prison sculpture with hundreds of illuminated candles inside. I look at the candles and try to think of something significant, a prayer for Mum, who soon will be two years disappeared, but nothing comes so I head to the bar. An attractive dark-haired guy in a stylish suit is sipping wine in front of the skull. Art Prince.

As I'm about to leave, Adrien calls and we arrange to meet at my place. Lamine is talking to a group of models and kisses me goodbye. Makoto and Chantal are near the exit and I kiss them too before taking the métro back to the Récollets. My studio is silent and warm. I cut up the Vegemite tube Dad sent and smear the remains on the dried-up end of a baguette.

It's close to midnight when Adrien finally arrives. He sniffs a piece of the cut-up yellow plastic and makes a disgusted face. I pour us both a small glass of beer.

He complains about the girl playing his lover in the play. 'She thinks it's okay to do whatever lines she thinks of. She doesn't realise I'm waiting for her cues! I lost my words completely!'

'I wish you could have come to the show,' I say. The beer gives me a bad taste in my mouth and I pour mine into his glass.

'Was it good?'

'It was okay. The best thing about the night was the motorbike ride through Paris. It was worth going for that.'

'You went on a moto?'

'Yeah, with Lamine.'

Adrien is silent. I go and brush my teeth and he sits finishing his beer. As I'm spitting, he comes into the bathroom.

'What's this?' he asks, holding out Harry's photo of me in front of the desert.

I wipe my mouth. 'Harry took that at his place. See,' I point, 'from where I'm sitting I look a bit like Uluru – you know, the big red rock in the middle of Australia.'

'When were you at Harry's place?'

'I don't know, back in summer. Remember? We watched a James Dean movie.'

'You didn't tell me you went there.'

'Yes I did – I called you from there, remember? You had that audition for the gangster show!' He is annoying me.

'No, you didn't tell me you were at his house.'

'Yes I *did*. It was after he did that crazy jump into the canal, we watched *Rebel Without a Cause* – I *told* you.'

'You are *lying* to me.'

My head hurts. He looks ugly, the gentle carving of his face turned hard, his eyes wild.

Controlling my voice, I say, 'What does it matter anyway, Adrien? Don't you trust me?'

'How can I trust you when you lie to me?'

'I don't lie!'

'You're lying to me right now.'

My face is hot. 'Look, Adrien, I'm sure I did tell you I went to Harry's, but if I didn't I'm sorry. But what difference does it make? It's you I love. Harry and I are just friends.'

'That's not the point.' He softens slightly.

We climb into bed and lie side by side, silent, staring up at the rafters. After a while he rolls onto me and holds my head tightly in his hands, looking deep into my eyes, and says, 'Do not fuck with me.'

'I won't!' I say. I feel scared, like he might hit me. We lie staring at each other, not blinking. His eyes fill with water. So do mine.

He hugs me. I'm confused, shocked, angry and horny at the same time. He takes off my clothes. An achy, but not unpleasant, sensation pulsates through my body. The muscles in our bodies are tight and I grip his biceps so hard I feel my nails break the skin. And then his red face and the veins and the sweat that drops in my eyes, and I die with him but it's too intense – a machine-like grasping that makes me want to scream. His grip on my arms is as strong as mine, only his nails are short, and I cry out as he expels his breath and rolls off me.

Instead of the usual calm I feel riled and pent-up. I want to punch something. Him. I've never wanted to punch a man. Right now, I want to smack Adrien. I want to kick him and shake him and scream.

I lie rigid beside him and let the feeling die down. He falls asleep. I toss and turn until morning.

Our breakfast is quiet. My mind races. What *was* that? Are we getting closer or breaking up?

'I need to practise my lines,' he says, stirring his coffee and not looking up. 'I should go.'

I can't have him leave like this. 'I can help you,' I say. 'It's a beautiful day. Why don't we go for a ride and find somewhere nice to sit?'

He pulls on his jeans and big coat and I put on a dress, two pairs of stockings and my doodoona, and we take a long, sullen bike ride to the Tuileries. It's an incredible day outside, cold yet vibrant sunshine, which of course makes the situation worse. Everyone is happy, rugged up in the sun with their families and lovers and grandparents and friends. We find two old green steel chairs near people throwing pebbles into a pond. Little boys float boats.

Adrien won't look at me. He takes out his crumpled script and we start running lines for his play. I find it hard to get my tongue around some of the words and my timing is slow.

'*Le médica-MENT*,' he corrects me. 'Please can you respond quicker.' He doesn't look up from his position bent over his spread knees, and we continue. My heart feels limp in my chest.

When he corrects me again I say, 'Fuck, Adrien! I'm trying.'

'Don't worry about it,' he says, snatching the script back. 'I'll get someone else to practise with me.'

My eyes prickle with tears. 'Fine. Find someone *French*. A real actor.'

'Okay, I will.' He rises.

But I'm not about to let him go like that. My blood is boiling. 'You know what, Adrien, I think we should spend some time apart.'

He turns and looks me in the eye.

I press further. 'I don't want to see you for a while.'

'Why? So you can fuck Harry?'

My fury boils over. 'Whether you believe it or not, I don't want to fuck Harry. It's you – I don't know you right now.'

'I don't think I know you either,' he says. There's a disdainful note in his voice that hits straight at my heart. It makes me even wilder. It's his fault he doesn't know me. He should have asked more questions. And he shouldn't have made me feel like I have to hide things. I want to provoke him to leave but the last thing I want is for him to leave.

I test him. 'Let's have some time apart.'

A breath of hesitation. Then he says, 'Okay.'

'*Good!*' I choke and march away, heartbroken.

I drift around the city for hours, through the quaint, enclosed arcades and mysterious backstreets behind the Palais Royal, ignoring memories of Adrien and Kiki and my early adult self. The air is bitterly cold, but hugged up in my doodoona I only feel it on my face. The sun disappears, and at Pyramides I walk down into the métro. The carriage is packed, damp and stuffy. I can smell at least five different types of body odour – light and fruity, tangy, rich, aged, *fennec*. When Adrien rides his bike to my place in the sun he whiffs his underarms and says, 'Whoo, smell the *fennec*.' Apparently it's a small desert animal.

My anger with him has already dissipated. We are both afraid. Perhaps neither of us expected to get into it this far; to be going to family Christmases, sleeping together almost every night, and yet not quite being real with each other. Well, me, not being real. And what next – when school is over? I'll have no visa. No financial support. No Récollets. What then?

A busker hops on with a set of speakers on a trolley and a rusty trumpet. He has an enormous black beard and is wearing patchwork jeans. A tourist and his teenage son stand shifting from foot to foot as the busker starts playing in their direction and dancing weirdly. He turns to blow the instrument towards me and I try to look away but it's a relief to have at least some airflow, and that's enough for me to give him the few centimes kicking around in my pocket. At Chaussée-D'Antin a huge swell of Galeries Lafayette shoppers get on, removing any relief brought by the previous exodus of passengers. When the doors shut I'm up to my eyeballs in shiny cardboard and strong perfume. The tourist and his son assume a new position closer to me and I notice that the man is dressed strikingly like my dad.

Dad. What will he be doing right now? Taking the dog for a walk on the beach? Sitting on his rock? Watching the footy replay?

As if hearing my thoughts, the busker begins singing an ear-raping baritone version of 'Non, Je ne Regrette Rien'.

It's uncanny how much the tourist guy resembles Dad. He couldn't possibly be French, in his baggy stonewashed jeans. A surge of affection rises inside me. I want to run and jump on him, bury my face in his strong, sure chest.

The busker exits with his jingly cup at Le Peletier and the tourist turns around to face me, relieved.

'Hey, are you Australian?' I blurt before I can think.

The man looks confused, then says, 'I – sorry,' with a thick Eastern European accent.

He and his son get off at Cadet, with an uncomfortable backwards look at me through the window. I collapse onto a newly empty seat.

⌒

For several days I do nothing but go to school, come home, get into bed with the curtains drawn. Nadine asks me to a party and I say yes and then don't show up. There's drinks at Faye's on Friday and I go for an hour then walk home in a daze, bumping into Harry, who is off to a bar to meet friends and invites me, but I say no. When he asks why, I choke up and tell him about Adrien. He calls the next morning and tells me to meet him downstairs in ten minutes with my bike. I say I don't want to go for a ride. He says get your bike. I say why. He says because I'm going to show you some Paris. But I've already seen Paris, I say. Go get your bike, he says. But it's cold, I say. Rug up, he says, and hangs up.

He leads me down the canal towards the Bastille. I've done this ride a million times and when we stop at the lights I pull up next to him and give him a bored look. He doesn't acknowledge me. We ride down the boulevard de la Bastille and across the river and into the Jardin des Plantes, which Kiki and I used to walk through before going to the Paris Mosque for mint tea and couscous. Harry gets off outside the Ménagerie and chains my bike to his.

I have never been to the Ménagerie. He buys two hot chocolate crêpes from the little stand outside and hands one to me. We go in and he shows me through a series of beautiful old pavilions containing crocodiles and monkeys and a lion, past flamingos on a lawn. He has a trajectory. At an outdoor enclosure with nothing in it he looks proud and points.

Huddled in a pack in a far corner is a pile of greyish fur. Oh god. Kangaroos. One stands and shakes all over before resuming her position in the pile of warm pouches and feet and fur. They shudder; the few of them that are awake look pissed off. *This is BULLSHIT*, they seem to be saying. They should be bounding across their scorched continent, annoying farmers, getting grilled on barbecues, not cowering here in Paris without doodoonas. What are they doing here?

I begin to cry. Bawl. Disgustingly. Crêpe hangs from my mouth. I want to reach out to the kangaroos but they are as far away from the fence as they can possibly be. I don't even particularly like kangaroos, but they suddenly look so familiar to me. They seem so clichéd when people speak of them in relation to Australia, I didn't realise I had a relationship with them. I can't believe I could feel this close to a kangaroo. And so far away. My hands clutch at the wire.

The tears won't stop. I am a marshmallow clutching wire and crying so hard my cheeks are freezing over. Harry doesn't know what to do. He stands near, with his hand on the back of my doodoona. I am choke-crying like a child.

'Fuck. I'm so sorry,' he says quietly.

I pull myself back together and give him a wet smile. 'It's not your fault.'

'What a dumb idea,' he says. 'I thought it would make you feel better.'

A kangaroo stands up from the pack and jumps around a bit. Then she stands in the middle of the field, looking at us. She has a joey.

We go back and get our bikes and I follow Harry around the park, beneath the skeletal trees, along the stones and then out a gate, past the light-responsive windows of the Institut du Monde Arabe, along the pale green-grey Seine, then eventually back across the river, through the Marais and up the canal to a bar called Le Jemmapes that Harry likes. We go in and he orders two Affligems from the bartender who knows him and we drink them down with our rosy cheeks and eat little olives from a glass.

'Sorry about that,' I say. 'I don't know what happened. It's nice you took me there.'

'Just trying to show you you're not alone here.'

'Thanks, Harry. But man, those poor kangas!'

He laughs. 'What a nightmare.'

To make up for it, he insists I come with him to his friend's party in the rue de l'Échiquier. I say absolutely not, god knows what he'll show me. He promises it will be wildlife-free. I go to the bathroom and wipe the mascara from my cheeks. No calls or messages from Adrien.

I go back out to the bar, where Harry is paying.

'Let me race home quick and chuck on a dress.'

The party is in a loft that was once a couture factory and has big industrial windows and cement floors. The people are older than me – like Harry, closer to their forties – and their style is more graphic-designer minimal, post-bobo. They lie around on cushions and lounges, comfortable in who they are. Their clothes are edgy, draped on their willowy frames. *Clothers*, Adrien says – he can't say 'clothes' – and I swipe him from my head immediately, though my stomach is in a knot.

In the bathroom a man in a bright green V-neck offers me a line of coke and I sniff it off a cover of *Numéro*. The sweet little rush gives me the confidence to talk to a whole bunch of people, including a Crazy Horse dancer from Bulgaria, a refined old actor with a lined face, a philosophy professor in red leather pants who chain-smokes grass, and a graphic-designer couple from Belgium with a three-year-old girl called Mathilde.

Harry keeps an eye on me, like a big brother. When hot food comes out of the oven he ushers me into the kitchen to get some first.

'Thanks for inviting me,' I say, nibbling at a cheese puff, though I have no appetite.

'Better than crying at home all night over your Frenchman.'

'Shut up.'

'Just a question, and don't get me wrong, I like Adrien, but what is it you see in him? Apart from his chiselled features?'

'Shut *up*.'

'No, I'm genuinely curious.'

I don't believe him but speak the words anyway. It feels good to try put it in perspective out loud. I tell him how at first I liked Adrien because he was so French and foreign, but then there was something else. As I talk about him my body rushes.

'Right,' says Harry. 'But don't you think he's a bit bourgeois? He's from a different world. I know that's a fucked thing to say, but things here are so compartmentalised.'

'That's exactly what his friends at their château thought about me,' I say, getting angry. 'I wasn't from their *world*.'

'Yeah right,' he says, backpedalling, 'it's all bullshit.'

I stuff down the pastry. I don't belong here either, in this million-euro apartment with all these stylish people. I don't even belong with Harry, in his humble, surf-guy clothes, with parents who own homes all over the world. I don't belong anywhere.

Later, after more lines and more vodka, I jump on the back of Harry's motorbike and we ride behind a group of people from the party to Montmartre, descending into the basement of a modest bar called Le Soleil de la Butte. The music is pumping and Harry and I dance and dance. He is so funny when he moves. We swirl and jump until the lights are up and chairs are on tables.

It's getting light outside as we ride down the cobbled streets of Montmartre, pulling up outside a dodgy brasserie opposite the Gare du Nord. We can't sleep yet and Harry says it's the only thing open. We sit dunking tired old chips into ketchup and sipping Leffes as the sun comes up. The beer tastes amazing on our dry tongues.

Harry's fingers are thin and smooth on his glass, which doesn't match his stocky frame. It feels good to laugh and mess around with a mate. Adrien and I never feel like mates. Lovers. Not mates.

Outside the Récollets Harry stops the motorbike and hugs me goodbye. I drink in the hug. My head is in his neck and I get the urge to kiss it. Harry makes sense in so many ways.

As if reading my thoughts, he starts kissing my neck and jaw. I allow it to last longer than I should, before pulling away.

I don't want things to make sense.

Harry laughs and I laugh back, still drunk. He holds out his warm hand and squeezes mine.

'Call you tomorrow, idiot,' he says, getting on his bike.

'Do that, fuckface,' I say, and watch him speed off down the hill. A streetsweeper approaches in his yellow and green uniform, swishing water down the drain. Another little piece of information to withhold from Adrien, if I ever see him again.

Café des Deux Moulins

After ten days I can't take the suspense anymore and call Adrien. We arrange to meet at the Café des Deux Moulins in the rue Lepic, the cute, cosy brasserie featured in the film *Amélie*, which has somehow retained its authentic Montmartre charm – so much so that the first time Adrien took me there I didn't recognise it. How it hadn't been turned into an amusement park baffled and delighted me.

It starts raining as I ride past the sex shops of Pigalle, which is infuriating because I've spent a substantial amount of time on my hair to create a natural, effortless look. By the time I arrive I'm a frizzy, frazzled mess.

The bar is welcoming and warm, and the corner table available, with its rocky legs. I am ten minutes late and he hasn't arrived. The waiter brings me a glass of saint-émilion that is overfull and spills as soon as he walks away. I mop it with a serviette and lick between my fingers, pulling out a crossword to try to keep my cool, though all I can do is stare at the words.

He appears in front of me, looking equally rain-messy. We kiss on both cheeks, like when we first met, and there is still electricity, but it's tamed. The corner mirrors reflect us to infinity. He sits opposite me, like we're having a meeting. He is different. More manly somehow, assured, like he's about to make a presentation. He orders a beer.

'How is school?' he asks.

'Fine. How's the play?'

'Fine.'

The small talk continues. If he still wants me he is doing an excellent job of concealing it. Then in the middle of the banter he tells me he's decided to move on.

Move on? I hadn't expected him to reject me. Now I don't know how to respond. I'm a demolition site.

There's a long silence, which he breaks by asking, 'What do you *want*, Jayne?'

'I can't really tell you that.'

'Why not?'

'Because what I really want is to sniff you.'

He lets the comment sit for a moment.

'Well, why don't you?'

I go around to his side of the table. He stays facing forward and I put my nose in his neck, running it up and down the thick pulsating vein that leads up to his ear. I drink him in, sniffing his jaw, his temple, his collarbone. I could eat his brains, I want to suck his mind out through his ear and into me so I can understand him, keep him. He is aroused by my sniffing and moves his hand gently to mine. I kiss his cheek seductively. Then I move politely back to the other side of the table.

'I have to go,' he says.

'Okay.' My muscles for his abrupt departures are by now well toned. We unchain our bikes and ride down the hill together in the gentle rain. I want to joke, 'It's crying,' but don't want to break the silence. Perhaps if I'm silent long enough he will stop his bike and ram me up against the wall. We stop outside the Moulin Rouge, where I'm to turn left, he right. Our bikes tip awkwardly as we lean towards each other to kiss goodbye.

The kisses are polite but our cheeks touch long.

We pull our bikes apart and go our separate ways. My heart is leaden as I ride through the rain, which is also heavier now. I don't need to cry. The sky is crying for me, down my cheeks.

Back at the Récollets, when I reach the landing on the second floor I see a dark figure outside my door, in a puddle.

Adrien.

'I need a towel,' he says.

I run into his arms.

~⁀o

We lie in tangled silence the next morning.

'Why do you think moths singe themselves?' I ask.

'They're drawn to the light.'

'Yes, but why?'

'They get confused by the bright lights of the city. They use the moon to orientate themselves. So when there are a thousand moons ...'

'You don't think they just want to get close to the light because it's beautiful?'

'Perhaps.'

'Would you rather live a short, exciting life or a long, unexciting one?'

'Long and exciting.'

'My mother died,' I say without thinking. 'I'm sorry I didn't tell you. I didn't really think ... Anyway. She died, not long before I came here.'

He sits up and looks at me. He is not angry, but shocked and curious.

I tell him the whole story, in French. Recounting it in a different language gives it a distance, like I'm telling someone else's story. But saying the words makes it feel more real. Us too.

Bourgogne

Séverine has a house in Bourgogne, which she should never have mentioned because ever since she did, I've been pestering Adrien to take me there.

'You have a *house*? In the *country*?'

'My *mother* has a house,' he corrects. She apparently bought it six years ago, did a bit of work on it then forgot about it. He hasn't seen it since.

I cannot believe that after all the summer heat and spring days, a house with trees around it has just been sitting there. Adrien and Séverine are sheepish when I press them on it.

Finally, one clear spring morning we're pulling out of her garage.

'It's probably run by beavers now,' says Adrien with a reproachful look at his mother as she changes lanes, cigarette hanging from her mouth.

Over the *périphérique* we go, through traffic jams, past factories, high-rises, grey monstrosities. Then the sudden onslaught of grass and space. I inhale deep. Near lunchtime Séverine pulls into a tiny supermarket in a village, where a lovely man with a nose shaped like a stingray serves us. We buy mustard and a lettuce and Adrien selects wine. I'm excited about the idea of roast potatoes for lunch and curious about the *côte de bœuf* Séverine is going to cook on the open fire.

We get back in the car with our bags and boxes and tear through the quaint towns and fields, then down a dirt track. Fields of green and yellow surround a little valley, where the remains of burnt vines dot the landscape. Behind a mansion, backing onto an apple orchard that backs onto a forest, is a small, fenced-off property. I can just make out the roof of a small house.

'It was a gardener's cottage,' says Séverine, grinding the car to a halt.

They call it La Grange. A wire gate with a big padlock has head-high dry grass poking through it. It seems to have completely taken over the place, like in *Great Expectations*. When Adrien pushes on the gate the grass pushes back. He gives his mother a look. He manages to open the gate wide enough to squeeze through, then disappears into the grass. He returns moments later with a grim-reaper scythe and cuts a track for us to the house. At the doorstep he throws the scythe on the ground, muttering, 'Disgrace.'

Séverine unlocks the door and goes inside, causing a great gust of dust to plume onto the dirty verandah. Adrien grabs the scythe again and starts hacking at the grass around the house, which I collect and clear out of his way. Silently we continue this for hours, him cutting, me collecting, until there's a huge pile of grass and sticks near the crumbling old shed, the roof of which has fallen in. His shirt is off and his torso like something from a calendar: *Hot Frenchies in Nature*. My ankles are covered in cuts and scratches. The sweet scent of hay and honey is in my lungs and I feel so happy I could burst. Adrien catches my eye and smiles. I want to lick the dirt off his body.

The front of the house is now visible: it's a pretty stone cottage with ten high, ivy-wrapped windows looking out over the garden. Séverine has opened all the windows up and calls from one of them: 'À *table!*'

Inside it's quaint and rustic. The floor is dirt-covered stone. Séverine has thrown a chequered cloth over the table and placed on it the *côte de bœuf*, two baguettes, a green salad, a big sighing camembert, and a melon for after. A glistening bottle of cider drips a pool onto the cloth.

I am ravenous from the physical labour. My mouth drools, my body rejoices. I sit down and have my first taste of *côte de bœuf*. The beef, grilled on the open fire, is still bloody; it's been sliced thinly and served with mustard. I savour it with gusto. Dad would fall off his chair.

The sunlight casts a shard across the table, across the delicious meat and vegetables, the mustards and sauces, the glasses of gamay, the old, worn cutlery. A large gilt mirror with rust patches is propped against the far wall and I look in it out of the corner of my eye, trying to catch my real self. The back of Séverine's head is in view, and Adrien's serious face, the two of them in discussion. I'm in profile between them, my hair lit white by the sun. That's me, part of the story. Sort of. That's me with the big silver knife about to cut the camembert the wrong way; there's Adrien's strong hand shooting out to correct me. That's me, slurping the I Need You, Adrien trying to explain the cute mistranslation to Séverine.

We smoke after eating, flushed from wine and fresh air. Séverine refills our glasses and announces that Adrien's cousin Valérie gave birth to her second baby yesterday. She looks at me. 'Will you have babies, Jayne?'

I take a sip of wine. 'I think so.'

'I was twenty-five when I had Adrien,' she says after an awkward silence. 'Now you are thirty you should get moving.' She leans in towards me. 'Maybe I'll have grandchildren.'

'Maybe,' says Adrien, giving her a harsh look.

'Would you have children here or in Australia?' presses Séverine, and Adrien sighs.

'Here, I suppose,' I say, feeling queasy.

'But your family,' she says, looking down at her nails. 'You will need them. You will miss your mother more than ever when you have a baby.'

My throat closes over. Adrien told Séverine weeks ago about Mum, and since then she has been sweeter and more delicate with me than ever. Now her eyes are cold.

'It will be hard to have your babies away from your home,' she continues. 'You will need your family.'

Adrien rattles his chair. I try to breathe but a guttural sob comes out. I try to suppress it, which only makes it worse.

Séverine leans across the table. 'Let it go. Let it go.'

I feel angry. Angry at her and angry at myself and angry at everything. Gathering control seems impossible: the more I pull back, the worse the coughing, sobbing sensation. My ugly performance lasts a long time. Adrien clears the table and comes back and puts his hand on my hands.

'You know,' says Séverine, once I've pulled myself together, 'my father died while I was pregnant with Adrien. It was terrible, I had this life in my belly and this grief —'

'I'm sorry,' I manage to say.

'It is okay to be sad,' she says. 'It's good to cry. It's nice for us to have a cry together, don't you think?'

I nod, though it doesn't feel nice at all.

⁓

The yard slowly reveals itself. There are fruit trees and rose bushes and another, smaller shed down the back. I hear birds, the rushing of leaves in trees, sheep bleating in the distance. In the late afternoon Séverine disappears, and returns later with a handful of apples from the orchard, throwing me one. It's sweet and juicy.

'I want to see the orchard,' I call to Adrien, and he drops his scythe and puts his hands on his hips, turning around to survey our work.

'Not bad,' he says.

We follow the neat rows of apple trees towards the forest. Something catches my eye and I grab Adrien's arm and we slowly crouch. A baby deer is eating from one of the trees, oblivious to us. I've never seen one before. I scratch my nose and she looks up, but she's too young to be afraid. We watch unmoving and then, when it's safe, we creep towards her. A little closer, a little closer, until we can nearly touch her. She is in a sort of trance, drawn to us. I go to reach my arm out to her and she's jolted back to reality, bounding off and disappearing into the forest.

'There are lots of them here,' Adrien says, and wraps his arm around my waist.

In the forest the last of the sunlight casts dappled shadows. We cross a stream into a mossy den heavy with mist, the sunlight far above us now, in the tops of the tall trees.

'*Je t'aime*,' he says, as we stop to kiss by a rock.

'I love you too,' I say, in my language.

That's Where it Is

After two years at his school I've realised that Jacques Lecoq would think my question of whether or not a corpse moves is a dumb one and doesn't warrant answering. It's a question that somebody who's living in their head would ask, not somebody consumed by play and art and fun and life. These entire two years have been an answer to this question, the answer being: Just move.

Our final project is to create our own piece of theatre and perform it for the public. We can write, direct or act, or do all three. There are no rules. I spend too long racking my brains for the perfect idea and run out of time. In desperation I pull out some of the writing I've already done. I dread using the piece called 'I'm Sorry, We Still Have Time', but hear Al say *that's where it is* and try not to overthink it. I bring it into the space and start thrashing it out.

I play the mother role, Marie-France plays me, and Meg and Faye and Sarah Israel play the inside of the me character's mind, as well as other roles, using pieces of costume to indicate the character changes. As the mother, I find myself wearing a scarf and always having my back turned to the audience.

Working with the text is agonising, embarrassing, shameful, but the more we physicalise it, and the more ideas the others bring to it, the less personal it becomes. It becomes a work of its own. Strange doctors are born, performing their own interpretations of oncology, radiology, haematoma, and all the weird drugs. The me character asks the mother character all kinds of banal questions, about the weather, dinner and television, while the chorus asks the true questions she wants to ask, like:

Does it hurt?

Are you scared?

Are you worried?

What are the red wings?

We create a weird opera about the uselessness of it all, with a stupid dance to go with it. There are bread ovens and toxic waste and huge needles. On the day of the performance I play my role with gusto, becoming more and more distant, until all that's left of the character is the scarf. Death comes and does a silent little jig. The movement of the corpse?

I don't know. I have no answers. Jacques Lecoq would be proud, I think, even if the piece was a mess. I just did it. I *bouged*.

The teachers don't give good or bad marks, say '*Stop!*' or 'Okay, *merci!*' this time. It's like a transition to a professional phase. We are no longer considered students; they are critiquing us as theatre-makers. There is no praise, no criticism, which at first feels terrifying, but then I realise how respectful that is. It has been like that the whole time. Never about us, personally, always about the work we are making. We have been treated as artists.

They tell me to keep pushing into the territories of the absurd, the tragic and the comic. And to keep writing.

And just like that, school is over.

I knew it was coming, but, like Mum's death, I didn't think it would actually happen. For two years my head has been down, my mission: get to school on time. Get into second year. Get a *bien*. Oh god, I haven't thought at all about what I will do now.

Meg, Faye, Étienne, Marie-France and I talk about forming a theatre company. But my visa will end next month, my residency at the Récollets will be over, my scholarship allowance will stop. I somehow have to set up a new life.

Daphné Papps

After several messages, Nadine's acting agent finally calls me back and says come tomorrow at noon and, whatever I do, don't forget my paperwork. Before I can say anything else she has hung up.

I forget the paperwork. My bowels pang as I run back up the métro stairs and across the blocked intersection to the Récollets, before sprinting back to the same spot, dialling Daphné's number.

'Well, *merde*, just *get 'ere*,' she barks. 'You have *wasting* my time with this phone call.'

I consider not going, but can't pass up the opportunity. Perhaps she's nicer in the flesh.

Daphné Papps Management is the ugliest building in the prettiest street in the 9th arrondissement. The shabby door in the back of an old courtyard has *DPM* printed on it in faded gold. I press a buzzer. A dog yelps inside and the door is ripped open, and a woman with wild grey hair leads me through a series of rooms as she rants in French/English about lateness and lazy actors. Daphné, Nadine told me, while French, lived in England for a long time, which is why she represents *zee anglophones.*

She rips a chair from under her desk and bangs it in behind my knees, lighting a cigarette. '*Understand?*'

'Yes,' I stammer. 'I really am sorry.'

She is scary-looking, though the distant echoes of great beauty are still there. Beyond the puckered anus mouth painted clumpy red, rotting nicotine-stained teeth and bulging glass eye, her face is perfectly proportioned and her grey hair long and thick. The office is damp, the walls also nicotine-stained, and the dusty desk is littered with filthy ashtrays. A picture of Daphné smiling with Charlotte Rampling is blu-tacked to the side of an old computer, which makes an old-fashioned hum. Charlotte smiles, reminding me of my insignificance. A fan blows stinky air onto the damp dog that comes to slobber on my knee.

'Bisou,' says Daphné, her face lighting up. 'Come here, you beautiful darling of my heart, yes *chérie*, I love you, come to Mummy, *oui, oui.*' And the dog pads over to her to receive a full-blown kiss on the mouth.

Then, like lightning, the bitch face is back on me.

'So why the 'ell are you in Paris if you are an actor speaking English? You 'ave no brain?'

I tell her how I plan to stay and work as an actor here, in French, English, whatever. How I want to mount a theatre company and make my own solo work too.

'And what about your papers?'

'I've got a student visa for now, but that's going to run out soon. If I get a job —'

'Do you have a boyfriend?'

'Yes.'

'Marry him.'

'Yes, but I don't need to —'

'Marry him.'

'There are other ways,' I say, but Daphné bats my words away with her cigarette, bending over to kiss Bisou. The loving face she shows to him returns to bitch face as she looks back at me. She tells me again to get married, it's the only way. I tell her I have it under control. She tells me to get out, she has another appointment. Then adds that I should get new photos – mine are *disgusting*.

If I enrol in the three-month French course at the Sorbonne I can extend my visa for that amount of time. That will be long enough to get a job and sort out my living situation. Adrien and I could pretend we've been living together and get a de-facto visa, though I don't want to bring this up with him, it seems so unromantic. I have, however, secretly gone to the town hall and got the cold pile of paperwork.

In the end I decide on the extension, but I have no intention of turning up to the classes at the Sorbonne, and not just because they start at eight am – I don't want to go. But I learn to my dismay that a new decree has been made, whereby you must have a near-perfect attendance rate to keep your student visa. So there's no option but to go to class, every weekday morning for three hours.

I'm surprised to find them interesting. I like driving my professor crazy with the street French I've learned. When he asks if I enjoyed my weekend I say it was *un truc de ouf quoi*. The others in the class need to learn *correct* French, Monsieur Carlieu says, but I keep asking why we're learning things that people don't actually say. I make it my mission to convert my classmates into real French speakers, so that they don't leave the course, as I had university, impotent in the real world.

Daphné sends me to weird auditions with briefs like *unpretentious foreigner, hungry cat that wakes in a glass box* (for a science fiction film) and *French-speaking American journalist that interviews Édith Piaf on a beach*. I get a call-back for a role in a touring production of Othello, but when they find out I don't have a long-term visa they give the part to a friend of Nadine's.

Papers, papers everywhere. Job applications. Attestations. Bank statements. Visa forms. Adrien sleeps soundly as I rifle through the pile, trying to make sense of them all. Two weeks until I have to leave the Récollets. No more money. I sigh and put my head in my hands, then walk naked to the window. The chestnut tree is at its fullest, fluttering with birdlife.

Adrien's head appears over the mezzanine wall. 'Hi you,' he says, rubbing his eyes.

'Hi.' I turn around, enjoying the sun on my back. 'Want a coffee?'

He smiles. 'Want to get married?'

'Ha!' I say, disappearing into the kitchen. I bring him up his coffee and flop on the bed.

'I'm serious,' he says, putting the coffee to one side.

In French you say *se marier avec*. You marry yourself with someone. Squash yourself together with them. Yes, I want to squash myself together with Adrien. But do I want to marry him? It would solve a lot of problems. Also, I love him. If I marry him we can stay together.

'I want to marry myself with you,' he says. His face is soft. His eyes are clear. 'I want you to be my wife.'

I put my hand on his cheek. 'I want to marry myself with you too!'

We stay in bed all morning, trying the idea on our lips and in our bodies.

'My *wife*,' he says. In French, *femme* – the same word as for 'woman'. Perhaps I am becoming a woman after all. A *madame*. Madame Masson.

'My *husband*.' *Mon mari*. The words resound, deep and mature.

I say he should call my dad. He looks sheepish but puts on clothes.

I dial the number and Dad picks up and says, 'Can it wait? It's the last half-hour of *24*.' I say no, it's important, and pass Adrien the phone. He goes downstairs and I hear the words 'I love yer dotter en I would like to merry her, if that is okay wiz you, and I promise I will be good to her and I won't take her away from you.'

I will marry him at La Grange in springtime in long grass with wildflowers and an outdoor lunch table with *côte de bœuf* and I Need You. It will be warm and breezy and my dress will move gently. I will have bare feet and hardly any makeup on. Kiki and Dad and Kate and the boys will come.

We talk dates, send 'save the date' messages, call our friends and family, get excited. Kiki says she'll come, and adds, 'Wow, you really are going to have baby croissants.' Kate says, 'I can't believe I don't know him.' My brothers both say, 'Congrats.' Dad says Adrien sounds very nice and that he guesses he'd better book himself a ticket.

Adrien takes me to the Brasserie Julien, the jewel of the Faubourg-Saint-Denis with its sensual curved doors and mysterious dusty hats in the windows belying an Art Nouveau treasure trove: carved mahogany chairs, polished bar with crêpe suzettes burning in silver dishes, red velvet banquettes, and tall, meticulously painted women curling up the walls. We order foie gras and champagne and steaks and wine and chocolate fondant and dessert wine, compliments of Dad. My stomach and soul burst with joy and a little apprehension about how we are going to do it all in our current financial situation. But I try to forget that. We talk about rings and let ourselves be wrapped in the opulence of old Paris.

On a hot morning in early July I hand my keys in to Chantal at the Récollets desk. She hugs me like I'm her child. Then, feeling like one, I take the train to Asnières, with my enormous suitcase and too many loose bags. In his apartment Adrien wraps his arms around me tight. Now we are a family.

There is not enough space for us both. I won't settle in too far – I have put notices up at the Sorbonne and in the English bookshops and the American Church, where I found my au pair job years ago, advertising English tuition, so I'm bound to get some work soon, then we'll be able to afford a bigger place, *dans* Paris. In the meantime, small pockets of space have been made for my shoes and my *clothers*. Adrien hangs my Special Dress under one of his heavy suit jackets. A few other dresses fit in the wardrobe, the doodoona on the back of the door, and the rest of my clothes in tight piles in the drawers he has emptied for me.

Everything must be put back in its place after use – I can't throw my jacket over the sofa when I come in, or leave my sandals in the entranceway. It is essential that the bed is made and returned to its sofa alter-ego every morning upon waking, or life will crumble. Bathroom time is structured and we are still discreet about pooping, and I get used to cold showers as the hot water is off again. Fragments of me slowly migrate to bookshelves, walls, drawers – hair ties and pins and long strands of blond hair.

There's just one thing that won't find its place, the orange A4 envelope with Al's photos of Kiki and me in the Dordogne. I don't know what to do with them. I'm afraid of what Adrien will do if he finds them, and yet I can't throw them out. They are precious, not only because they were taken by such a famous photographer, but because I love them. They're awful, and impossible to look at – I haven't so much as glanced at them since the day I showed them to Kiki – but they're a tiny piece of us. I'd give them to Harry to hold onto, but what if he looked? Nadine might lose them. Marie-France too. I have to keep them near. Though I may never look at them again, they will forevermore go everywhere with me.

To hide something from my future husband makes me feel uneasy. But I can't see any way around it. I put the envelope in a pocket in my suitcase.

Girl of the Night

It's Bastille Day, *quatorze juillet*. The day is stinking hot and we're lying in the park on the slope of Montmartre, under a tree, eating sandwiches. Adrien's head is on my belly and I'm stroking his hair, which leaves my fingers greasy and smelling of coconut. I sniff them and kiss his temples. Our toes are bare. Adrien's have huge bulbs at the end like E.T.'s fingers.

'Pleeease!' I plead. Adrien's aunt Béatrice is having a party at her Trocadéro apartment, with its view over the Eiffel Tower, to watch the fireworks.

'I don't like Bastille Day. A lot of my friends don't.'

'Why not?'

Because, he says, it celebrates the murder of a large number of people.

'But doesn't it also signify the end of the aristocracy living it up while people were dying in the streets of starvation? The creation of liberty and equality and fraternity for everyone?'

'Yes, but still, a lot of people were killed.'

'Right. But can we go see the fireworks anyway? Please?'

'Okay, princess. I like to watch them too. Plus Béatrice always has excellent wine.'

We finish our sandwiches and ride to Trocadéro. It's a beautiful evening. The Champs-Élysées has red, white and blue flags all the way down it, like in the painting by Manet. People are parading, shouting, full of Frenchness. I remember marching up the Champs-Élysées with throngs of jubilant people after France won the 1998 World Cup, shouting as though I was one of them and feeling like a phony. I still do. I doubt that even marrying Adrien and raising children here would ever make me French enough to own a World Cup victory. I have decided to stop trying. Speak the language but let go of the pout, accept the smile in my voice, drop the dead eyes in the métro. I seem to be approaching a place where I can speak French and participate without having to annul my personality at the same time.

We reach a cobblestoned street with a steep incline and chain up our bikes. It's an attractive modern block, perched on one of Paris's rare mini *buttes*. We shoot up the lift to the top floor.

The door to Béatrice's apartment is open. Nobody is inside, they're all out on the terrace. Around the enormous living room are dozens of bottles of champagne in assorted boxes and bags, tied with ribbons, in ice boxes, on benches and shelves. Thank goodness we didn't do as I suggested and blow twenty euros on a bottle of champagne, to be polite. A woman in a black dress and apron is placing hors d'œuvres on a platter amid the crowds of bottles. '*Bonsoir messieurs-dames*,' she says and trots out onto the terrace.

The room has a 270-degree view over Paris. We are very high up. The wraparound terrace is wide, jutting out over the rest of the building. I grab Adrien's arm and we walk out together. It feels like we're floating in the sky. We stand gaping at the Eiffel Tower, which looks so close I could jump onto it. It's lit up with blue stars. The sky is darkening.

'Your city is a wonderland,' I say, gazing out.

'It's your city too, now.' He kisses my neck.

'Get a room,' says a voice in a British accent. Xavier, Adrien's peacock of a younger cousin. He launches into his usual fast-paced English in an attempt to emasculate Adrien and impress me. Adrien smiles, unfazed. I don't want to speak English with Xavier and exclude Adrien, so I talk back to him in French, despite his persistence.

Another voice calls from the crowd and Béatrice emerges to kiss Adrien and me tenderly on both cheeks. 'But what, no champagne?'

she says, flitting off to find glasses. We clink just as the fireworks begin, then stand mesmerised for forty-five minutes, each burst of light and sound exploding my entire soul. A trillion sparks in all different colours, dancing and lighting me up. Somehow the display is not clichéd or trashy with its grand effects and daring formations. It's magical.

When the show is over, Xavier says, 'Last year's was bigger.'

He asks me about the summer and I tell him about the two new English students I've secured, a shy banker whose first name is Williams and a jewellery maker named Sophie, who looks like a porcelain doll. He tells me he's going to sell handbags with Gigi at the Puces de Vanves, and I could work there too, if I needed extra cash.

'You have to be there at five am,' he says. 'I don't mind, I rise with the sparrows.'

'Not me,' I say in French as Adrien listens in. 'I'm a girl of the night.'

A woman sitting on a chair next to us makes a loud tut-tutting sound. 'Be careful what you say,' she says, shaking her head.

I turn to look at her properly: an attractive woman in her late thirties, wearing expensive-looking evening wear, smoking a long cigarette. She has big red lips and an aquiline nose. It seems she has been observing us for some time.

'*Excusez-moi?*' I say. 'Are you talking to me?'

'Yes,' she says with a sophisticated drawl. 'You should be careful what you say.'

'I don't understand,' I say. The boys shuffle with embarrassment.

'You say you are *une fille de la nuit.* That means something particular in French. People get the wrong impression.'

I would normally apply a She Who Smiles Last nonchalance to this kind of interjection, shrug it off and keep talking with the boys, extra loud, with as many double entendres as I can inject. But I'm drunk, mildly stoned, and irritated that she thinks she has the right to impart her wisdom to me. Adrien and Xavier try to change the subject but I ignore them.

'A whore, is that what you mean?'

'*Allez chérie*, it's not important,' says Adrien under his breath and tries to turn me back to the view.

'No, I really want to understand. You think I'm not aware of that meaning?' I ask the woman. 'Is it not obvious I'm not a whore?'

The woman shrugs. 'I say just that in France, people they hear things and they think things. You have a very loud voice. You should be careful what you say. That is what I say.'

I want to pick up her chair and toss it and her over the balcony, but I manage to keep my cool. 'Well, I think the inference is funny. Don't you have a sense of humour?'

She smirks and continues drinking, sitting there alone. I turn to the boys and say loudly, 'How rude was that?'

Neither of them answers. Then Adrien mumbles, 'Why didn't you just ignore her?' He seems uncomfortable, which shocks me even more.

'Because she was being rude!'

They both remain silent, and my insides boil, my knees turn to jelly. That sensation returns of the world melting away from beneath my feet. Where *am* I? A minute ago I felt at home. Now I'm an alien again.

Adrien tries to hug me. 'Look, maybe she's right – sometimes you should be more careful of what you say.'

I go rigid. Xavier laughs and lights a cigarette. I make an excuse and push past groups of laughing and talking people to the bathroom and lock the door. There is a big white bath. I imagine it sprayed with my blood. Face in hands I sit and try not to scream, then go back out to the kitchen, pour myself a glass of water and signal to Adrien out on the terrace: *Let's go.*

Cheers and cracking sounds fade behind us as we ride towards the outskirts of Paris. I want to tear off in the other direction, arm above my head, middle finger raised, or ram him off his bike and punch his sculpted face in.

We ride silently down the boulevard Malesherbes. The night feels dead now, there are no cars, no people, and the closer we get to the *périphérique*, the stiller and quieter it becomes. As we cross the Seine I stop and scream as loud as I can, in English, '*PARIIIS! FUUUCCKKK!*'

Adrien stops his bike and turns around. Then he surprises me by joining in, screaming out over the river in English too. '*Helllp me! Paris! PLEEEASE!*'

Cars toot as they pass us but we keep screaming until it hurts and then fall to the ground. He grabs my hand and I push it away, then grab it back and bat it away again. I try to kiss him and he pulls away, then takes my face with his hands and holds it hard, staring at me. I shove him roughly in the chest. He looks shocked. I urge him with my eyes to shove me back. He gets on his bike and starts riding. I get on mine and follow him in an obsessive fury.

My stomach is tight through the streets of Levallois, he pedals like fury and I follow. I don't want to go to his apartment, but where else can I go? The nowhere feeling is huge, though I know this street so well. That old stone wall. That apartment block. That garage. That dark boulangerie. A sensation of being alive pangs through me, of being nothing but in this moment.

His eyes are shining as we pull our bikes into the lift. He stares at me like an animal. I look straight back at him. I wonder if we're about to kill each other. We cram our bikes roughly into his entranceway and his tongue is suddenly deep inside my mouth. My hands grasp at his back.

'You drive me fucking crazy,' I say, pushing his body off me.

'You drive *me* crazy.' He pulls off my dress and presses himself roughly against me, I scratch and bite at him, tearing at his skin and hair. My back is raw the next morning from couch-burn, my head somewhere else.

～

The strange energy between us builds over summer. We go stir-crazy in his apartment and can't afford to go very far. He drives me to the beach at Deauville in Séverine's car: we get sunburnt as lobsters and come straight home. I leave my clothes on the bathroom floor, which makes him seethe. He keeps playing a new French pop song I can't stand. He says I overcooked the spices in the dhal I spent hours cooking. I get a searing urinary tract infection on a Sunday when all the pharmacies are shut and have to spend the afternoon lying in Séverine's bathtub, pissing myself and feeling more insecure than ever before. She's in Algeria on a shoot, thank goodness. I lie for hours in her manufactured warmth.

After an altercation over the misplacement of his tweezers I suggest one autumn morning we ride to Montmartre, thinking it might lift the mood, and after lunch in a charming, rickety café high on the hill, we return to our bikes to find that his has been stolen, the lock that had been woven through mine cut clean in half. He is furious, and storms off down the hill, as if in search of the culprit. I follow, telling him there's nothing he can do, but he gives me a death stare so I let him continue his pointless trajectory and ride back to the apartment, and, not knowing what to do, clean it from top to bottom. He doesn't say thank you, which annoys me and leads to another tiff. He says sorry and then we fuck and feel a bit better.

The end of summer is cold and rainy. Séverine returns from her long shoot and we arrange to go to the country house. We walk towards her place hand in hand, not talking. Adrien seems nervous.

Séverine's lips are tight when she kisses me hello, and she is steely in the car. On the highway Adrien sends me a message from the front seat: *I feel my mother may not support our marriage.*

I thought it was strange that she hadn't contacted me since Adrien told her the news. I assumed there was bad reception in Algeria. I feel gut-punched. What happened to her enthusiasm about me having babies? I'd have thought she'd be thrilled we're heading in that direction. What is she afraid of? That I'll be too old to give birth? That I'll take Adrien away to Australia? Did she find out I pissed in her bath?

It's cloudy when we arrive at La Grange. It is starting to look like a real home, but weeds have sprung up in just a few weeks, and there's still a lot of clearing and pruning to do. Séverine heads straight inside to keep working on the floors. Adrien and I garden into the night before falling into bed, oversleeping and waking after eleven. The bed is cold and damp from the overnight rain; water leaks down the wall opposite. I dreamt of Mum on a highway, walking towards me but never getting closer. Again, though the dream is frustrating, the worst part is waking having forgotten she's gone. I cling to Adrien but his back is stiff.

After breakfast, discouraged by the garden having turned overnight to mud, Adrien and I decide to go to an antique fair in Gien. He's in a terrible mood. I hug him as he bends over to tie up his shoes and he jolts me off. I can't remember the last moment there was softness between us.

He's probably upset about Séverine, I tell myself. It must be terrible to feel that your mother isn't happy about your engagement. Does she think he's doing it to help me stay in France?

It's deserted in Gien and we park on a muddy slope just near the *brocante*. He asks if I want a chichi. I say what's a chichi. He says, like a churro. I say what's a churro. He hands me a paper bag of greasy donut sticks dipped in sugar. I eat one, then go to hand the bag back to him so I can take a closer look at an old clock, but the chichis drop in the mud. He huffs and picks the bag up, tosses it in the bin.

The *brocante* is boring. I buy a pair of books on saints for ten euros and we leave, stopping on the way home at a pretty fortified town called Sainte-Geneviève-des-Bois for groceries. We walk back to the car across a lovely bridge surrounded by fragrant flowering bushes. I think of Mum and my dream, and of Dad throwing her ashes into the river beside the holiday house we used to rent. We'd all stood on the bridge and tossed flowers we'd picked from the hill behind the house, watching them drift with her dust out to the sea. On impulse I pick a flower now, close my eyes and throw it in the water.

'You shouldn't do that,' says Adrien beside me, and my face gets hot. I watch until the flower is gone from sight, then turn and walk silently back to the car. He cleans the mud off his shoes with a stick and gets in, slamming the door.

Mum wouldn't have liked it either. She hated it when I picked flowers from other people's gardens, or public places like hospital driveways. I got a beautiful collection from outside the cancer unit once and she made me not only throw it out, but hide it in an outdoor bin so nobody would see. 'You mustn't *do* that!' she said to me when I returned to the room. But I always thought flowers were meant for everyone.

'You're right,' I say, anger in my voice. 'It was a really dumb thing to do.'

This gives him the permission he needs to let off some steam. 'You don't take care. You just fly around, do what you want. But some things are important.'

'Right.'

'You just do what you want,' he repeats.

'Yes.'

'But what about what other people want?'

'What do *you* want, Adrien?'

His hands clench the steering wheel.

'Perhaps you don't want to marry me?'

He lets out an exasperated sigh. 'I want to marry you, Jayne.'

'But you don't trust me! You think I'm a whore of the night! And I can't even show you the dumb photos Al took of me and Kiki, because you'll think we're lesbians! You think I'm careless when I throw flowers! I kissed Harry! Well, he kissed me and I didn't really kiss him back, but still! I feel like a bad person! Like I'm cheating on you all the time! And I'm not! I'm not!'

He hunches over the wheel, breathing hard. I don't know which of those comments hurt him the worst.

'And your mum hates me.'

'She doesn't hate you, Jayne.'

'Well, it doesn't matter now anyway. You hate me.'

A pause. 'Maybe you're right.'

Yes. Now he's said it. He actually hates me. And I hate him. I still want to fuck him. But I hate him. Great place to start a marriage.

My lips are tight and my eyes well with angry tears. 'Did you mean that?'

'Perhaps,' he says, distant.

'Maybe you should have thought about that before asking me to marry you.'

'Perhaps I should have.'

He pulls up at the house. Séverine is chopping wood and waves to us. 'She is not part of this,' he says. 'She is not part of us.'

I push the onions off my knees and storm off into the forest, staring blankly at the apple orchard, looking for a deer. The sun comes out and shines on my face. No more slave labour. I go back to the house and pull on my swimsuit and lie in the garden in the limp rays of sun, drinking a beer, watching him and Séverine hoe together. Fuckem. Tom Waits growls into my earphones.

Adrien comes over, drenched in sweat, and takes a sip of my beer. 'I like your bikini,' he says.

Like nothing has happened.

The Pussy Knows

Getting stuff off my chest was a relief but it doesn't make things better. Adrien doesn't want to see the photos, though I pull out the orange envelope. They're probably worse than he imagined. I store them as deep as I can in my shallow storage. We are on edge. Engaged still, by a membrane. Still fucking and dying. Talking little. Wondering if this is the start or the end.

I get three new English students through Sophie, the jewellery maker. Adrien gets a new job in an exclusive restaurant where all the big stars and producers and directors go, and he can get them drunk and high and make them fall in love with his waiterly good looks and give him roles. He is the whore of the night. I'm jealous. I never used to get jealous. I want to be the starlet on that velvet couch. But Daphné has nothing for me, even though our marriage-intention papers are in. Adrien works late. I give my English classes and watch reality TV.

Gabriella, my best friend from drama school in Melbourne, comes to Paris to celebrate her engagement to Marcus, an Australian soap star who has been also living in LA. Their ballet-pink 'save the date' card with our names in calligraphy is stuck to Adrien's fridge. They are staying in the 10th so we meet them at La Marine, the magical restaurant where I had my twenty-ninth birthday, a lifetime ago. Adrien was so sweet that night and we were so soft, touching each other's hands beneath the table so nobody would see. Now the tension between us is palpable, exacerbated by the ease between Gabriella and Marcus, who understand each other without explanation or compromise. Their effortless banter bounces back and forth, and conversation between the three of us flows like water. We're relaxed in our own language, fluent in our own culture. Adrien has the pleasant, distant face I so often have with his friends. Nodding, smiling, not quite there.

On the back of the toilet door is some excellent graffiti: *Exterior wealth can never camouflage interior poverty.* True, I think to myself, but it would pay for this dinner. *Nik tout* feels more relevant: *Fuck everything.*

In bed that night we lie stiff beside each other. My hole seems to have closed up. The pussy knows.

I push Kiki out of my head. This has to work.

⌒

Adrien has a small role in a film being shot at Versailles. He sends me a photo of himself smiling in his decadent costume: he could not be better cast. I am on an aimless bike ride around Paris wearing Mum's Special Dress, which is completely impractical but was all I had clean. It flies out behind me like a colourful '70s sail.

The sun filters through the trees along the busy boulevards and narrow streets. I follow my nose down to the Seine, and find myself at the river past Notre-Dame, where I first really saw the view that day at twenty-two, but it seems the spot has disappeared, like a portal.

I end up near the Pont Neuf, where the river cruises take off every hour. On a whim, I lock up my bike and get on one. Without the trees for protection the sun is potent and I sweat in the dress, sun stinging my forehead. It's lunchtime, and this is a French-language cruise, so there are only two other people on board: a couple of American tourists who got it wrong. The young Russian hottie reads her script into the microphone with as much enthusiasm as if the boat were full. A hot breeze moves the light silk fabric around my legs as we skim across the water. I've never

JAYNE TUTTLE

seen the city from this angle, peering up at its backbone, ribs and lungs. It feels intimate, like I'm inside her.

Being off the land gives me a new perspective and I feel present in the moment. Just here, right now, empty seats all around me. The city stretches out on both sides, modest and grandiose, aloof and inviting. She likes my dress. In this moment, alone with Paris, everything feels perfect. I'm at one with the city, not pretending to be someone else, not trying to be French me or Australian me, just me. Adrien asked me to come to Versailles and spend the day with the cast and crew, Séverine being one of them, but I told him I had class at the Sorbonne, which I did, but I didn't go. If he knew I was here right now he'd think I was having an affair. Am I?

I flash back to the night I met Adrien, the enigma of him in the doorway. The dashing Frenchman. Did I translate him into what I wanted? Now that I'm no longer peering through the veil of culture, I see the outlines of a sensitive young man, who loved me at first too, but who also translated me into something he wanted, a nice young lady who would fit into his world. I try to picture Adrien in Australia. I can't. Or myself in a nice apartment in a nice Paris suburb, doing nice things. Paying bills, feeding children, doing dishes. No. It doesn't hold. I'm trying to put bricks and mortar around a fantasy world.

I think I want to be real again.

The weather starts getting cold again. Daphné sends me to an audition for a marionette theatre in the 20th. It's a long ride, involving Ménilmontant, a steep hill that reminds me of the one the man heaves his wretched body up in *The Triplets of Belleville*, training for the Tour de France. But I could use the train money and, though it's chilly, I need the air.

'*Merde*,' says Adrien as I leave, which is how you say 'good luck'. You're not allowed to say *merci* in return, so I give him a tight smile and leave.

Paris is shrouded in a thick, cold mist. I push hard and fast through it, getting damp and sweaty, all the way to Belleville. On Ménilmontant, I ride for as long as I can before I'm forced to dismount, somewhere around the rue de Tourtille – it's just too steep. Even pushing the bike is torture. The pavement is narrow. I pass the Chinese restaurants, trying not to knock over their A-frames advertising the day's lunch menu. An old lady swears at me and gestures wildly with her arms when I almost hit her as she steps out of a doorway.

The theatre is old and dusty, like the puppets. A family of meticulously crafted dolls that, even as they lie in their boxes, look alive. Antonio, the director, takes us through a warm-up and then shows us how to work with the different characters, their joints so refined that when manipulated correctly they move with lifelike precision. We spend hours experimenting with them and afterwards I am exhausted. The physical effort and concentration required to be a *marionnettiste* is immense – you must become the puppet. There is nowhere to hide. As in the neutral mask, every small shift in your being is magnified in the doll's. You have to be *juste*.

Antonio shakes my hand afterwards and offers me a job, starting January. I say yes without hesitation.

I'm in a very good mood when I leave the theatre. The sun has come out and cleared the mist, leaving the air sharp and the sky a stunning winter blue. My heart is full. I have a job! At the top of the hill everything seems perfect for a moment, and the glorious feeling stays with me as I sail from Saint-Fargeau along the avenue Gambetta, right past the rue Pelleport, where Sophie, my favourite English student, lives.

I think about calling in. We've become more like friends than teacher and student, spending most of our class time chatting over drinks in cafés around her neighbourhood, or in her apartment, which is full of light and dainty things. Sophie is the most genteel woman I've ever met: she says, '*Mince!*' when she drops a pencil – 'Drat!' I love exploring her place, with its high bookshelves and interesting artworks and the delicate jewellery she makes, hung on nails in the wall. Last week I stayed for dinner after class, making friends with Lou, her shy little five-year-old, who has the same pale skin and delicate demeanour. She asked me to bathe her that night and I did, creating underwater kingdoms with her mermaid and ship.

Sophie would be happy to see me, but I decide not to stop. I want to get back and tell Adrien about the job. This regular money will change things for us. Things are back on track.

I turn into the rue de la Chine, a one-way street with a mismatch of old and new buildings, and am riding up the footpath when a handsome, forty-something man steps out in front of me.

'*Désolée!*' I say, dismounting just before I hit him.

'*Op – pardon,*' he says, wiping his brow. He is renovating a corner restaurant and is covered in plaster. In the window is a notice that reads *Appartement à Louer.* He sees me looking.

'Looking for an apartment?' he asks.

I nod. Am I?

'It's the American upstairs,' he says. 'She put the notice up half an hour ago.' He buzzes the intercom before I know what's happening. 'Carrie? It's Luc. There's someone interested in the apartment. Go up,' he says to me. 'Have a look.'

I hesitate, but find myself pushing on the open door to the first-floor apartment, where an overweight American lady in a fuzzy, peach-coloured jumper sits on a worn couch, halfway through a bottle of bordeaux and a *Voici* magazine.

'Hey there!' she says. 'I'm Carrie. Come in, sit down!'

I look around at the mottled peach wallpaper, the heavy marble tables, the astounding collection of porcelain frogs. Aside from the décor and walls, it's a lovely little apartment, perfect for one big person or two small ones. The poky salon has old raw floorboards, there's a separate bedroom for sleeping, and there are plain but pretty windows with curled iron boxes outside to put flowers in. The lady asks if I live around here and I tell her about the audition and Sophie and my recent visits to the 20th.

'It's a fabulous quarter,' she slurs, 'I just lurrve it. I have to go to Spain, then to Texas to play grandmamma, and I won't be comin' back here. Can you afford seven hundred a month?'

'Yes,' I say, gulping. Seven hundred is perfectly reasonable but I don't have a cent. 'I'd just need a few weeks to get the first month's rent together, and the deposit. When is it available?'

'Right now, sugar,' she says. 'You know, the couple downstairs that run the restaurant, Luc and Clémence, are just darling. They sure have some fine wine down there.'

'Is there anywhere to store things?'

'Oh yes, sweetie, there's a *cave* downstairs. Lots of room down there.'

'Would you mind if I moved some of your furniture down there? And painted the walls?'

'Of course not, darling, you can do whatever you like. It would be yours. I understand that you may not like frogs quite like I do.'

I give an awkward smile and she laughs and refills her glass. 'You know, honey,' she says, 'you seem like you're somebody I could trust. It ain't easy to find good tenants around here. If you wanted to go ahead and move in, you could pay the deposit later. And if you need some time for the first month's rent, that's okay too. My instincts are good. I know you won't let me down.'

This is so kind and unexpected that tears spring into my eyes. 'Gosh,' I say. 'Thanks.'

'I'll be here just a few more hours. You could even move in tonight. It's all yours, honey.'

I blink and look at her, wondering if she's serious or just a bit tipsy. She looks back at me with total sincerity, setting down her glass.

'I'll go home and talk it over with my fiancé,' I say. 'Then I'll call you. But it really does seem perfect.'

She gives me her number and a hug, which feels nice – motherly – though her jumper itches like hell.

'Bye, honey, you be sure to call,' she says as I walk down the stairs. I wave to her as she closes the door. It already feels like home.

In the doorway I thank Luc, and walk my bike slowly down the street, taking in the buildings around me. It's a charming, unpretentious street. The neighbourhood is far quieter than the 10th, but noisier than Asnières. Quintessential Paris. *Dans* Paris. I turn right and walk down a smaller street, past older beautiful buildings and newer plainer buildings like Carrie's, with their perfunctory Parisian features. I pass a quaint bistro with an open fire lit inside, and a little *brocante* store selling old furniture and knick-knacks that I imagine filling the apartment with once the frogs are cleared. I turn onto the rue des Pyrénées and walk beneath the tall bare trees, past fruit and cheese and pastry shops, crossing the street to follow the fence line of the Père-Lachaise Cemetery. Adrien loves cemeteries. He will love it here. We can renovate the apartment together and splash paint on each other like in a romantic comedy. We can wake in the morning in a bed that we don't have to fold up. We can hang up the beautiful white curtain and it will blow lightly in the breeze. We can plant flowers and buy a record player and eat in the bistro with the fire on Friday nights. And after our wedding we can return to the apartment and make croissants on the floorboards in the moonlight. Sophie and Lou can babysit.

I wander back through unknown streets towards Belleville, looking in doorways and behind gates, lost in thought. On the steep rue de Belleville, I go to mount my bike and realise with panic that my phone has been switched off since the audition started. When I turn it on I'm shocked to see it's nearly six pm. There are seven missed calls from Adrien.

'Where *are* you?' he says.

'I'm sorry,' I say, throat tight. 'I got sidetracked on the way home. Something amazing has happened! I have a big surprise for you. And guess what else?'

'What?' he says flatly.

'I got the job! I'll tell you about it when I get there. I'm on my way now.'

'Where are you?'

'Still up in Belleville. But I won't be long.'

'Are you telling me the truth?' he asks.

My jaw clenches. 'Of course,' I say, and hang up.

I push off, deflated, but determined to get back quickly and make things right. From up this high on the hill, I can see the Eiffel Tower glimmering in the distance, like a jewel at the end of the rainbow. I ride dangerously towards it down the steep hill, across the boulevard and down through my old neighbourhood in the 10th, which feels still and empty, pedalling hard across the canal and past République, hurrying towards Asnières.

As the streets grow wider, I pedal harder, and the faster and further I go, the more something opens inside of me, as though the motion is removing something heavy and constricting. Something seems to have blown off me in my rush. My jaw unclenches, my brow softens, and a new sensation fills my body, something light and free. I am alone. And also, deliciously, not alone. As I fly along I feel a strong sensation of Mum being with me. And Kiki. My sister, Kate. Dad. My brothers. Australia. My heart feels full of light and a burning joy. The limits that were binding me seem blasted away. Australia is right there, I can go back now. Paris is right here. Mum has disappeared, but she is here. Kiki is gone but not disappeared. Everything is okay. Everything is perfect.

I pedal on through the city, hitting a traffic jam as I arrive in the Place de l'Opéra. The sun has started to sink, leaving the sky a burst of intense oranges and pinks. The grandeur of the square is intensified by the glory of the sky, and outside the fairytale Palais Garnier I'm not sorry that I have to dismount and walk my bike to the island in the middle of the intersection, to wait for the traffic to budge. I stand in wonder, gazing at the merging colours above the dreamlike palace with its sculptural homages to the gods, the great arts and artists, losing all sense of time as the traffic honks and blares around me. The golden angel of poetry lifts her wings high on the top of the building, set alight by the dying sun. Her svelte shape burns into my eyes.

As the traffic starts to flow again I mount my bike. Then, as though the bike has made the decision for me, instead of heading towards Adrien's I find myself turning back the way I came.

Back to Belleville.

Back to the rue de la Chine.

Harry brings a big bucket of white paint and four rollers. Marie-France brings a potted wild geranium and helps with the first coat of paint before running off to her rehearsal for a travelling play. Sophie and Lou help me plant the geranium and some cheap roses in the window boxes, though Sophie says they won't live long in the cold. They stay all afternoon as Harry and I paint, wrapping tissue paper around each of Carrie's frogs and placing them in boxes, which Fred, Sophie's quiet and serious husband, later carries down to the cave for me, along with the marble table and the heavy, dreary lamps. Luc from the restaurant downstairs brings a box of beer and he, Harry and I drink it sitting on the drop-sheets with loud music on, before Luc leaves and we do a final coat of paint. You can still see patches of the wallpaper beneath, but the place feels mine.

After a week, Adrien comes. When I didn't turn up that night he was furious, then confused, then sad. The phone calls followed, the emails, the text messages. Then, silence. We weren't moving in together. We weren't getting married in long grass. Just as something inexplicable had brought us together, it was now keeping us apart. It was decided. I missed him viscerally, curling up in the new bed as though I'd had my core removed. It was a hot pain, unlike the stillness of Mum's cold death. It seared and scorched.

He stands in the doorway, handsome as the night I first saw him. My heart still pounds. I ask him in. He puts my things neatly in a corner, looking around. The place is nice, he tells me, *c'est cosy*. I invite him to sit on the couch. There is some *saucisson* and bread on the table and I offer him some. It is ending, as it began, with sausage. He takes a piece and starts peeling away the skin, which he doesn't normally do. I point this out. He shrugs and eats the sausage. I take the skin for him and put it back on the plate.

When I would tell people at parties that the night Adrien and I met was the first time I'd eaten meat in a decade, he would squirm and later say, 'Don't you get it?' Of course I did. That was why it was funny. The more he squirmed, the more I'd say it and the more I'd embellish the story. It pained me to see him cringe but I couldn't help myself.

Perhaps I thought if I pushed him hard enough he'd come around to the other side. Perhaps I was testing him. Or perhaps I was trying to push him away.

But I did love him. I loved him in a powerful way, a way that defied the constraints of the day-to-day, defied logic, defied earthly concerns. There was something in him I wanted, that I knew was in there but could never touch. I still know it's in there but I know I can't get it.

Looking into his face, I sense that he feels the same. He felt me, deeply, too, felt some fire in there he wanted, but in the end I was just a normal person, with an annoying desire to embarrass him. He needs a nicer person. I was going to say, like Marie-France, but she is defiantly not nice, and would smack me for insinuating it. A nicer, *Frencher* person.

Stop looking into my eyes. Like that night at Odéon, his eyes are locked on me, but there is a new obstacle between us now. Someone else on the telephone. But that desire – still there. Damn that desire.

He kisses me on both cheeks in the doorway. A thousand tiny pins of electricity.

The following weeks are dark. I can't bring myself to tell anyone at home what's happened, and on Christmas Day I sit in the cold apartment, eating hot noodles from a cup. Dad lent me the money for the bond and the first month's rent, and I don't have the stomach to borrow more, so the heating is off. If I can just get through the holidays, work will begin at the marionette theatre and all will be wonderful.

The Sorbonne classes keep going through the holidays, so I get up for my eight am phonetics lesson in the dark and take the métro across town. I don't have enough money to go to the movies or sit in a café, and it's too cold to be outside in the park, so I make my way slowly home each day to the noodles and the silence. Harry is in Australia, Nadine is at her housemate's country manor for Christmas, Marie-France is at her grandparents', Sophie and Fred and Lou are in Normandy, Luc has shut the restaurant and the neighbourhood is quiet. The street lamps come on at around four pm and cast their light through my window boxes, creating long, curled patterns across the floorboards. My favourite place to sit is in the salon, looking at the patterns, back against the cold cement wall. I must not call Adrien.

A pile of letters arrives one day, which he has redirected to me. Wedding acceptance letters, each a stab in the soul. 'Delighted!' 'Excited!' 'Thrilled!' The letters fall around me in a listless pile. Every day I come home and allow myself to open a few more. Each one brings a different kind of pain.

One cold evening, I open a pink envelope. Inside is a Christmas card from my nan. To my ecstasy, enclosed is a twenty-euro note. I jump up and rip a cartwheel through the salon, almost knocking a wall out.

As if my sudden movement has woken the dead, for the first time in weeks my phone rings. It's Sophie. They're back. She asks me to come for dinner.

Guillotine

'*Mademoiselle?*'

The woman leaning over me keeps saying *mademoiselle*, and I keep answering *oui*, but she can't seem to hear me. Perhaps because she is under water.

'*Mademoiselle* —'

'*OUI!*'

This time she hears. '*Mademoiselle?* You can hear me?'

'Yes, I can hear you,' I say in very polite French. She isn't wet anymore. I am. I'm wet all over. Everything is wet. I'm lying on a floor. On my back. Something warm is dripping in my ear.

'You have been in an accident,' the woman says, her brow furrowed. 'What is your name?'

I tell her and she says, 'Good, Jayne, we're going to get you some help. I am Eveline, a nurse. I live here in this apartment block.'

The sound of wet footsteps thudding up the stairs. Sirens blare, voices murmur in different places around me.

'Was there a bomb?' I ask. I want to sit up and look around but I can't feel my body. My breath is short. The woman smiles, holding my hand between her two hands like she's protecting a tiny baby bird. I can see my hand but not feel it.

'Don't worry. Everything is okay,' she says.

The dripping in my ear is now a steady running. The woman's face looks strange, her features won't stay still, they pixelate and fade. Then everything is black again.

A handsome face is above me. A *pompier*! Finally, a Paris firefighter, come to rescue me.

The woman tells him, 'Her name is Jayne.'

'Jeanne?'

'Jayne. *Une Anglaise.*'

He can't pronounce me. 'Stay with me, Jeanne,' he says.

Yes, I will stay with you. I love you. God, I love you so much. I will love you forever, *pompier*, even if you can't pronounce my name, even if we make no sense.

He asks me to move my fingers and when I try I gasp; I'm falling back into the dark again, into the dark and wet, a drain.

A light shines in my eye. Another face moves into view. Sophie! Her hand is on her mouth. Her face is white as white. 'Oh Jayne,' she squeaks, eyes wet.

'*Ça va?*' I ask. 'Is Lou okay? Is there a war?'

Her head disappears and though I have the urge to follow it a voice says in my head, Just look forward. Lie very still.

The *pompier* is here again. Hello, my love.

'Keep looking in my eyes.'

Yes of course, my love.

'We are now going to lift you down the stairs. We need to fit a neck brace. This will not take a moment.' He smiles. There is movement behind me. The trickling continues in my ear and I want to rub it, but the voice in my head says not to move. I let them do what they are doing. I can't feel anything.

My body begins to rise in the air. There is red on the wall. Now I am floating down the stairwell, backwards, watching the dim grey walls, the lift cage, the carpet, Eveline's worried face withdrawing. Someone keeps turning the volume up and down, *woWOwoWO*.

Look at the wall, the voice instructs. Just keep looking at the wall. Black.

'*Mademoiselle?*'

They won't let me stay in the drain. They keep saying *mademoiselle, mademoiselle*, over and over, it's driving me crazy.

'*Mademoiselle?*'

I'm in some kind of van. Tubes and sheets: an ambulance. The doors are open. We are not moving. I can just make out the dark and misty sky.

Sophie's voice is beside me, talking in muffled French. 'I don't know. Her face. Her head. They don't know. I don't know! Oh Fred ... On the staircase. I don't know why ... fainted. No, I don't think she understands. To Tenon. Lou is with Eveline.' She stops speaking and sobs into her hands, loud and gutteral. I try not to listen. People outside the van are shouting. Lights are flashing.

I whisper, 'The elevator.'

'Jayne?'

'It was the elevator,' I croak again. 'The light. It was dark. I was excited. I wanted. To see Lou – wanted her to see me. I got stuck, my head, the rail ...'

'*Ohmondieu,*' she says in one breath.

There is a long pause.

'Who should I call?' she finally asks.

'Adrien.'

As we tear dramatically through the streets of Paris I feel fine. I've always feared something bad happening to me here, thinking how terrible it would be to be far away from home. But now that it's happened, it's okay. Paris has looked after me before and she will again. Look forward, I tell myself, don't think about it.

'We're going to the hospital now,' shouts the *pompier* from the front seat. Someone beside me pats my hand. I keep looking straight ahead.

At the emergency entrance a team of people run out and lift me onto a trolley. They are all silent and serious and don't look at me. They wheel me into a room with very bright lights, past people who stare and put their hands on their faces. Now Sophie is with me again, holding my hand. Her hand is clammy. There is a fine, crooked crack in the ceiling. I fix on each craggy little angle: it's a river through Central Australia. Sophie leans over and looks into my eyes. I tell her not to worry, I am fine. She nods slowly. Her eyes are glassy.

Everything is okay. Nobody is dying. Nobody has cancer.

They wheel me through a series of corridors and the lights keep flickering and going off. We pass a man with a huge bump on his head who is screaming very loudly. There are other screaming sounds and I wonder if I have been brought to the madhouse. Now we're in a darkened room that feels as vast and empty as the gym at high school and they wheel me to the back corner and pull a curtain around me. Faces come to loom over me, look shocked, then disappear. I am clearly a horror show. The screaming and moaning from the man in the corridor mounts. Someone shouts, '*Ta gueule,*' and he shuts up for a moment. Then he starts whimpering, before building up to a loud moan again. The lights go on and off, fluorescent bands flicking, strobing. Sophie sits next to me, silent, white, holding my hand. I'm not sure why she is so upset. I'm fine. I smile at her and she looks shocked.

'Have you ... has ... anything, like this, ever happened to you, before?' she suddenly blurts.

What does she mean? Have I put myself in unnameable danger before? Stood on a railroad track? Shot myself from a cannon?

'You just seem so ... okay,' she says. 'You keep smiling.'

I *am* okay. I am happy. A strange ecstasy is burning through me, a brightness, like I've just been born.

She moves closer to me. 'I'm pregnant,' she says and smiles as a tear runs down her cheek. 'I just found out today.'

'Congratulations!'

We sit in silence again for a few minutes and she caresses my hand. 'If only,' she says, then stops.

If only what? She hadn't been running late? If only I hadn't been on time? If only the man hadn't arrived when he did and pressed the button for the *ascenseur*? If only he lived on the third floor and had a saying *Under four, lift's a bore*? If only the dim stairwell lamps had been replaced just once since 1933? If only the lift hadn't been recently serviced, making it chillingly silent on descent? If only the liftwell had been enclosed? If only the stairwell rail were higher? If only I'd never come to Paris in the first place ...

But Sophie never finishes her sentence. 'I have to go,' she says. 'I'm sorry. I'll come again.'

'Okay,' I say.

She kisses me and leaves, her footsteps interrupted by a warm male voice outside my cubicle.

Adrien.

The lights go out, it's black, but I know I'm here because I can hear Adrien's murmur and Sophie's sniffing interjected with deafening bellows from the man in the corridor. Panic sweeps through me – I can't see the wall – I don't have anywhere to look. Nausea swells and rises.

The lights flick back on.

Adrien.

His face is kind. He is wearing his long dark coat. His beard is at my favourite length. He sits down and looks me over.

'*Oh la la mademoiselle*,' he says. 'What happened?'

He is my family here, the only one I want to see. He is real as real, standing there in the flickering light, more real than he has ever been. Perhaps we are friends after all. I am so grateful to see him, tears spring into my eyes. I tell him about the elevator.

'*Bi-zarre*,' he says and rubs my arm.

The lights go off completely. When they flick back on Adrien is gone.

⁓

Now there's a nurse at my side, come to clean my wounds. She is very stressed.

'*PuTAIN*,' she says as the lights flicker again. 'It's fucking *Baghdad* in here.' She washes my head, saying, '*Oh la la la la*,' with continuous *la*s as the extent of my injury is revealed. I still feel fine. I can't feel my body. There is a salty chemical smell. I look ahead and don't think about it. Nobody has cancer.

The lights flicker and turn off, flick back on. I'm happy. But the nurse has returned with a grave look on her face. She tells me in a slow, loud voice that I need to be transferred urgently to another hospital, where they have the facilities to deal with my condition.

My stomach clenches. The voice says, Just look at the wall.

A team swoops in and rushes me through the corridors and out to another ambulance, another set of doors. This time, as the ambulance tears through the city, I feel every cobblestone, every crack, every cigarette butt in the street beneath me. The trip is purple, my stomach is a rock, the smell of mothballs is overwhelming.

Just look ahead.

They take me to Salpêtrière, the old lunatic asylum. Perhaps I *have* gone mad. A new team runs out and wheels me inside, leaving me in a corridor. My head is starting to throb and it feels sticky, like I have a piece of clingwrap around it. I hear lots of swearing. It's astonishing how much the doctors and nurses swear. I'm backstage now, I have never been here. The light is bright. A man in a white coat is inspecting my head. He has a lovely warm face.

'*Oh la la la la*. So you had a little altercation with a stairwell this evening, *ma chère*?' he says. I love the way he pronounces *ma chère* with a very long, old-fashioned 'airrr' at the end.

'The lift,' I squeak out. All my muscles seem to be tensing up, my throat closing over. 'I don't know. I got my head. Caught. Under it.'

He raises his eyebrows and sits down on the bed and takes my hand. 'And you pulled yourself out, they tell me. That's how you hurt your face?' he asks.

'I must have. I don't know.'

'*Un miracle*,' he says, with a serious look. His face is all delicate bonework, like a woman's. 'My name is Rigolette,' he says, and I know I'll never forget that name, as *rigolo* means fun. 'You are going to need some surgery on your face. But first you're going to have some scans, to check everything else is okay. Do you have any other pain, besides your face?'

'Um, my neck is really sore and stiff, like I've slept funny.'

'Move your toes.' I do, and they move slightly. 'Move your hands like this.' I manage to move them.

'If zero is no pain and ten is the most excruciating pain you've ever had, what level is your pain?'

'Eight.'

'Right,' he says. 'We'll get you something for that.'

A boy nurse and a girl nurse come in, laughing and bitching about someone, using lots of brilliant swear words and expressions. I wonder if Mum swore like this behind the scenes. They pull back the sheet, then they take off my lovely boots, my socks, my jeans. They don't take off my underpants. Then they look at the top half of me and sigh.

'*Désolé*,' says the boy nurse. 'We have to cut.'

It's my favourite red jumper, with the printed image of the unknown person on it. Some think it's a little-known image of Che Guevara. Some think it's the violent kid from *Flatliners*. I don't care who it is, I just like the bell-shaped sleeves and the high neck that keeps me warm, especially on the bike. My favourite bra is underneath.

Snip, snip, from the wrists all the way up to the armpits and down the sides. It feels sacrilegious, destructive. My breasts are exposed but

I don't care. I am no longer a woman. I just want to get better. They put a pale blue gown made of Chux over me, straighten the sheets and leave.

Adrien comes in. Warmth runs through me. His presence makes these past two years real. He makes everything real.

'Could you call my dad?' I say.

He shifts in his shoes. He doesn't know I still haven't told Dad we broke up.

'Maybe we should wait for the scan, to know exactly what the situation is,' he says.

'Good idea,' I say, and he gives me a weak smile. Now I don't feel very well.

They wheel me into a dark room and Adrien sits next to me. The light from outside the door casts a stripe over a medicine chart on the wall. I try to concentrate on it but it's giving me nothing. A strong disinfectant smell hits my nostrils, causing my stomach to clench.

'I think I'm scared,' I tell him.

'You're going to be fine,' he says. 'Try not to think about it.'

Just look forward, I tell myself, look forward. But it's not working anymore. A tear drips down my cheek. What will the surgery be like? What has actually happened? What did I do to my head? Have I ruined my face completely? Look forward. Why did I do it? *Had* I wanted to die? Stop thinking. You're going to be okay. You don't have cancer. Can I move? Will I walk again? I want to touch my face and the thought makes me sick. The fluorescent lights come on and a nurse walks in with a trolley with lots of plastic instruments and packets. Adrien leaves for a cigarette.

'*Bonsoir madame*,' I say.

'*Morphine*,' she says flatly. '*Vot' cuisse*.' A jab in my thigh.

White now, instead of black. Love washes through me like a warm wave as I glide through a hallway under rows of stunning lights. I am whisked into a lift and down through a maze of cement hallways to a beautiful concrete room. The clock on the wall is *tick-tick-tick*ing and I love the clock so much and I love being on the trolley and being wheeled around. And I love the nurse who says, 'Ten more minutes,' and the man heaving and coughing on the trolley next to me and the sensation of the cold sheets against my hands and feet and the feeling that my skin is still on my body – most of it. I love that I am going to be okay. That I have so much to look forward to.

'*Allez ... op op op!*' says a man with a magnificent face full of rivers and rocky crevices, as he helps me onto a tray in front of a big pizza oven, and my neck is so sore but I hold my head still as I move from one tray to the other, and I laugh as I say, 'My neck is *really* sore!' He feeds me into the oven, like Mum went into the oven that sunny day in February, and I wondered then if they would burn the casket too – what a waste! I lie there for a moment thinking of all the beauty of life – perhaps she was as peaceful in the oven that day as I feel right now – and then I am out and lying there for a glorious minute before they put me back on the trolley, and my neck hurts incredibly this time. But then it's better and I lie there for a very long time, ecstatic at the simple beating of my heart. To be alive is extraordinary and I feel that no matter what happens from here, the beating of my heart right now is enough. I could lie here forever and revel in its throb.

Then, like magic, I'm floated back into the lift and into the same room as before. Adrien is there. His arms are across his chest and his chin is down.

Rigolette sits next to me and cocks his lovely head. 'I have bad news,' he says.

I look at Adrien but he won't look at me. Terrible thoughts run through my brain. Is it cancer after all? Neck cancer? Face cancer? Did something happen to my brain? What am I doing here in this strange hospital in this strange country, with strange people around me, a man who's not my fiancé anymore, not my family?

Rigolette puts a hand on my shoulder. 'You have broken many small bones in your face and have some wounds that are going to require quite a bit of surgery. But you have a bigger, more serious problem. You have fractured your spine. Your C2.'

'Oh,' I say. What does that mean?

There's a pause before he explains that the C2 is the second vertebra, that I have a hangman's fracture, and then he goes off in a whole lot of words I don't understand. Then: 'We will know soon what is to be done, another surgeon is looking at the scans. For now, we need to operate on your face, it is important to do that quickly. *Ça va?*'

'*Ça va*,' I say, but my body has melted into the bed. Are they suggesting I may not walk again?

Look ahead. You don't know yet. Anyway, your heart is beating.

'I just need to have a good look at your face now.' He turns to Adrien. 'You might want to wait outside.'

But Adrien says, 'I have no fear.'

I'm glad he's staying. I need him to watch and tell me later.

Rigolette bends very close to my face, and with extreme focus touches a part of my cheek. I feel something warm on my ear, like peach flesh. Like cheek flesh. My flesh. Could that really be the flesh of my cheek touching my own ear? The feeling is cannibal. I look straight at Adrien, desperate not to know. He is pale but watching closely. I have a sensation of being very open, of air rushing in, like into a big canyon in the desert. Rigolette taps me gently on the head. 'Okay, back in ten minutes.'

Adrien comes to the side of the bed with his eyebrows raised.

'Don't tell me,' I say. 'Not even eyebrows.'

'He's going to do a great job,' says Adrien, patting my arm.

Rigolette comes back. 'I have some news about your neck. Your C2 is definitely fractured, but the fracture is not displaced. This means you will be fine, you will walk; you can have surgery or wear a special brace until it heals. You are young, you will heal. You do not need surgery. It will just take four months of patience.'

A sense of relief and wonder runs through me.

'You are very, *very* lucky, *ma belle*,' he says solemnly.

'Yes,' I say.

'I have no idea how your fracture is not displaced – I assume it occurred when your neck came in contact with the lift. But then you fell down a flight of stairs! And we have been moving you around ...' His voice trails off. 'So lucky. A miracle.' He pats my arm and disappears.

'I think you should call Dad,' I say to Adrien.

'Okay,' he says, rubbing his neck. 'But tell me the words.'

⟝⟞

Rigolette comes back in with the two nurses. 'Now I'm going to give you some needles in your face, then we're going to do a beautiful job of you. I just need you to turn very gently this way.' He carefully turns me onto my side with the aid of the nurses. Adrien isn't allowed to stay. The boy nurse gives me his hand to squeeze. I look forward. Rigolette jabs my right cheek and it stings. He jabs again near the first jab and it burns. He jabs again close to the other jabs and it pricks. The boy nurse has to leave and he looks in my eyes and says sorry, replacing his soft hand with a squeezy rubber ball. Rigolette jabs deep in the same place on my right cheek and it pangs inside my soul. Then he says, 'One more!' It prickles.

'*Et voilà*,' he says. He bounces his thumb in various places, asking me if I can feel it, and when I don't anymore he says, 'I'm going to cover you up with this cloth, don't be afraid. We're nearly there.'

But the stitching takes hours and hours. I can feel him, sewing, sewing. I am a lampshade, I think to myself. I am a skin suit. I am no longer human, just a ball of flesh. I squeeze the thing in my hand. Rigolette talks to me like we're in a knitting circle together and I talk back. We even laugh. He tells me to keep still or he will sew me up like an imitation handbag.

Afterwards I feel brave, noble. Adrien comes and peers at me. 'Wooow,' he says. 'You have thousands of the tiniest stitches I've ever seen. How did he do that?' When he has finished admiring my stitches, he takes my hand. 'I have to go now,' he says. He has an audition early in the morning. I ask if he wants me to test him on his lines but he says no. He tells me everything will be okay, gives me a kiss and leaves. I never see him again.

⟝⟞

I wake in a room full of light. My eyes can only open a crack. On my bed sits a female figure. *Mum.* She smiles. Her hand is on mine. My eyes begin to adjust to the light and I see that it's not Mum, it's Kate. My sister. She smiles at me. Her hand on mine is the warmest sensation of my life.

I have been fitted with a contraption that at first made me feel suffocated and want to scream. A *corset-minerve*, it's called. In Australia, they tell me, it would have been a 'halo brace', with bolts drilled into my head. The point is, the neck must never move. My brace is very recent technology. Dense, moulded plastic winds around my back and ribs, meeting at the front with velcro strips that are tightened. Around the back of my head, joined to the plastic strips down my back, is a solid headpiece that stays in place using a thick velcro strip that tightens across my forehead. A chin piece made of plastic is attached to a front bodice by bolts, which can be adjusted to keep it exactly in place.

Kate looks at me in that Mum-nurse way, unphased by what she's seeing, though I know it's bad. I don't want to look yet.

Because she actually is a nurse, they will let her take me out of hospital after a week and home to the rue de la Chine. The ambulance men will carry me on a stretcher past Luc's kind, shocked face and the concerned looks of the neighbourhood people. I will be placed in my bed and my room will smell so nice and Kate will let me sleep for days and days, administering the drugs and washing me down. Many days will pass and she will gradually lower the pain relief and I will hate her and cry but she will soothe me. The pain will be intense but it will be real and I will slowly return to reality. It will snow outside and I will start to eat again, the beautiful food that Kate has cooked, and she will take pleasure in coming back to the apartment with new delicacies she's found in the local shops, and stories of her experiences trying to communicate in French.

'The man told me off for touching a peach!'

'How many kinds of chicken can there *be*?'

'Can wine this cheap really be good?'

Kate won't let me take off the brace, though I beg her over and over. It is making me insane, I am in a cage, and then one night, without her knowing, I loosen it, just to sleep. I wake to a giant standing over me. Bellowing.

'*Do you want to be dead? Worse?*'

I whimper but the giant looms higher.

'*DO YOU WANT TO BE A BODY WITH A HEAD ON IT THAT CAN DO NOTHING BUT BLINK?*'

The giant shrinks and becomes Kate.

'I'm sorry,' she says. 'But I don't think you realise how serious this is.'

'Okay,' I say.

She tells me a story of a man on a highway. He is driving along with his family when a car comes out of nowhere and collides with them head-on. His family are all killed instantly and he is thrown through the windscreen and lands metres down the road. Everyone in the other car is also dead.

'Is this *Wild at Heart*?' I interrupt. 'I think I know this. *Wild at Heart*. David Lynch.'

'Shut up,' Kate says and goes on with the story. The man is in the middle of nowhere but he can see a house in the distance. Astonishingly, he's able to pull himself upright. He is in a sort of trance, caused by shock and adrenaline. Carefully he begins to walk towards the house. He knocks on the door. A woman answers.

'There's been an accident,' he says.

'Where?' she asks.

'There,' he says, and turns his head to point to the wreckage. And in that instant he falls to the ground, dead. He hadn't realised it but he'd fractured his C2. If he had kept looking forward he would have been okay.

Point made. I promise not to take off my brace.

Kate continues to be stern and vigilant; she does not want to take me home in a body bag, she says.

I keep my word, even when ants crawl through my veins as I come off the morphine and the cage makes me want to rip my skin off. Kate is patient and brings me books and tea and little roast birds she's bought from the butcher and cooked in the toaster oven.

One day I manage to stand up for a few seconds before fainting back onto the bed. After many panic-stricken attempts I take a few steps, and eventually reach the bathroom. A yellowed, sewn-together pile of flesh greets me: two black tracks of stitching fork out from a point just inside my right ear, towards my cheekbone and eyebrow. Another track lines my chin and there's another beneath my bottom lip. My right eye is black, and around the stitching are swirls of dark blue and black and yellowish orange. The hair on the front of my head is caked in thick, blackened blood – no wonder my scalp is itchy. My right ear looks as though it has nearly been ripped off. I swoon and feel vomit rise. Kate sees it and ushers me swiftly back to bed.

People visit. Harry sits at my bedside and tries to make me laugh. Friends from school come, teachers. And, after a long time, Sophie and Lou.

They stand in the doorway of my bedroom, not wanting to enter, as if the displacement of particles caused by their moving towards me might result in my crumbling to a pile of dust. I beckon them in and they walk carefully, Lou's tiny fingernails digging deep into Sophie's stocking. Sophie manages to bring her around to the front and wrenches her onto her lap as she sits on the rickety blue chair next to me. But that means I can't see her, so she sits on the floor across from me instead, with Lou safe between her crossed legs.

'We have a present for you from Eveline,' says Sophie. 'She has been very worried about you.' Sophie gives the package to Lou, who stands and brings it to me, running immediately back to the safety of Sophie's legs. It's amazing to think that Eveline is a real person and that I had been real to her.

It's a book. *Monsieur Caramel: Chroniques Parisiennes*. On the cover is a badly photocopied photo of a simple Paris courtyard with cobblestones and a cat. Inside the front cover is an inscription: *Pour Jayne, A story of a building and life in our quartier. Bon rétablissement! Eveline.*

The idea of reading a pleasant story about life in our *quartier* right now makes my stomach turn. I thank them and put the book aside.

After three weeks in the apartment, Kate thinks I am fit enough to fly. She spends a week packing up my belongings, puts the keys in the mailbox and holds my hand in the ambulance to the airport, and all the way back to Australia.

Dad is at the gate, face pale. He hugs me delicately in my cage, and people stare and murmur as I pass. He brings me back to his new little house by the beach, where we live like an old couple, watching television, eating meat-and-three-veg, reading books and walking to sit on his rock. The locals are intrigued by the walking robot-girl, and one day, as much for my pleasure as theirs, I walk into the sea fully clothed in my brace and disappear beneath a cool wave.

I am unpacking a bag from Paris some time later when I come across the book Eveline gave me. The back cover tells me it's about an old man whose wife dies, and rather than see out his days at home in the countryside where his family has lived for generations, he moves to Paris, into a tiny apartment in the 20th arrondissement. *A light, refreshing book*, says the blurb. *A confection to be devoured.*

Stomach tight, I decide to read it. Seeing the French words on the page gives me a pang of extreme, conflicting emotions.

The epigraph, by Jacques Yonnet, reads: *To penetrate the heart of a city, to grasp its subtle secrets, one must brush against her with the most infinite tenderness, and a sometimes exasperating patience …*

What was Eveline trying to tell me? That I should be tender and patient with Paris, though she nearly killed me?

Monsieur Caramel, now that his life has taken a new turn, is seeking something exciting, something unfamiliar. The apartment he rents in a modest building in a humble street is just big enough for a few belongings and his cat. He makes friends. He borrows a drill from his young female neighbour. He helps Madame Planchon perfect her monologue for the gates of heaven. He lives a simple daily life in his *quartier*, discovering his favourite boulangerie, wandering the nearby Père-Lachaise cemetery, talking to random people in cafés and parks. He is old, and living close to death, so his appreciation of every moment, down to the most banal, has a magnified importance. A newcomer to Paris, he is able to see the beauty in even the smallest things.

I drink in the book like a treasure. Perhaps Eveline was trying to show me that Paris heals, sometimes in mysterious ways. You must be patient, you must persevere.

After three months at Dad's the brace comes off. Tests show that my spine has fully healed, and with time and care should not cause me any pain. My face has also healed, leaving a neat scar from midway up my right cheekbone into the hairline above my right ear, and a few smaller, unnoticeable scars on my chin.

If you didn't look hard, you would never know I had been in an accident. But I know, and I'm glad the scars are there to remind me. I don't want what happened to feel like a dream.

Dad and I walk to his rock and sit on it, watching the waves. Like before, I have no picture in my mind of what I'll do next.

'Perhaps you could study to be a spy now. Or prosecute French criminals.'

'I definitely won't be able to act for a while.'

'Sorry about that,' says Dad.

'It's okay,' I say. 'I'll figure it out.'

When we get back that evening there's a message in my inbox from Marie-France: *I know you're recovering, but I just got a commission to put together a play for a festival in summer in Paris. I propose we make a full-length play of 'I'm Sorry, We Still Have Time'. If you can't act, can you write and direct?*

One month later, I'm on a plane to Paris.

Jayne Tuttle is a writer who splits her time between France and Australia. After graduating from the Lecoq Theatre School, she lived in Paris for more than a decade, working internationally as an actor and writer and publishing stories about life in Paris in newspapers, guides and magazines. She currently works for Paris advertising agencies as a bilingual copywriter.

Acknowledgements

Thank you to Melissa Kayser, and all at Hardie Grant Australia and UK, for bringing this book to life.

To my brilliant editor, Meredith Rose, and my indefatigable agent, Benython Oldfield, for their persistence and passion.

To my husband and creative partner, Matt Davis without whose eye, patience and endless encouragement this book would have no spark.

To my other most important collaborator, Frankie Davis, my daughter and eternal inspiration.

To my mother, Lyn Tuttle. I wish I could share this with you.

To my grandmother, Niela Laws, reading the dictionary in the sky.

To my beloved family: John, Anna, Rodney and Andrew Tuttle. To Christine Tuttle, Luke Elliot, Anna Hedgcock and Emily Tuttle. To all the Davis family.

To my creative inner sanctum: Marisa Purcell, Mary Kelly, Jemma Birrell, Martine Murray, Anna Elliot, Leigh Whannell, Corbett Tuck, Luke Davies, Kate dan den Boogert, Ashod Simonian.

To those who shaped this book with their friendship, support and creative guidance: Libby Little, Angelica Mesiti, Mathew McWilliams, Sylvia Whitman, Krista Halverson, Michele Davis-Gray, Michael Shmith, Paddy O'Reilly, Toni Jordan, Elsa Morgan, Nick Robinson, Rachael Coopes, Lucy Wadham, France Lane, Kate and Mal Heppell, Alice Retif, Kitty Walker, Suzie Wyllie, Alice Barker, Marylou Gilbert, Luke Milne, Michael Bula.

To Nathalie Delhaye, and Rose.

To SD, for the beautiful adventure of those two years.

To Chrystel Dozias and the Centre Les Récollets in Paris, for being my mothership all these years.

To France, for giving me the mystery grant, that to this day I still don't understand.

To the École Internationale de Théâtre Jacques Lecoq and my friends and teachers there. To Faye Lecoq, who supported and encouraged me always.

And to Jacques Lecoq, in spirit.